Probeware Lab Manual
for Computers and Calculators

D1457070

Prentice
Hall

Needham, Massachusetts
Upper Saddle River, New Jersey
Glenview, Illinois

ISBN 0-13-058529-7
3 4 5 6 7 8 9 10   05 04 03

Contents

© Prentice-Hall, Inc.

Introduction

All of the labs in this lab manual have been created to directly support your curriculum goals. Initially, you may find that students progress slowly but as they become familiar with the software and hardware, the benefits of doing probeware labs will quickly become evident. Students will analyze their data more readily and will reap the rewards of a much fuller conceptual understanding.

The *Science Explorer Probeware Lab Manual for Computers and Calculators* is designed to meet your needs whether you are using PASCO®, Texas Instruments, or Vernier hardware and software. The CD-ROM in the front of this Lab Manual contains User's Guides, experiment files, and electronic labs to make it easier than ever to get started and to enjoy productive lab experiences.

On the following pages you will find an introduction to each type of hardware and software. Additional information can be found in the User's Guides on the CD-ROM.

As always, safety must be the highest priority in the laboratory. Please make sure you and your students have reviewed the safety instructions and guidelines in Appendix A before working in the lab.

PASCO® Hardware and Software

The DataStudio™ software (purchased separately) works for all experiments, all subjects, and all levels with the use of PASPort probes and sensors. The versatile DataStudio software runs on Windows and Macintosh platforms. Based on teacher preference, your students will use either an appropriate DataStudio Workbook or the preset DataStudio Configuration File.

The DataStudio Workbooks provided on the CD-ROM are designed to integrate seamlessly into your unique classroom setting. These workbooks provide all parts of the labs (problem, materials list, procedure, analyzing data, and extensions) on screen and seamlessly integrate the technology in a user-friendly interface. The content, structure, and underlying processes are based on the *Science Explorer* textbook.

The CD-ROM also provides DataStudio Configuration Files, which can be used with the printed laboratory worksheets in the PASCO section of this book. The worksheets provide all parts of the lab, and the configuration files automatically set DataStudio to the necessary parameters. All your students need to do is plug in the correct sensor, open the correct file, and start collecting data.

DataStudio Quick Start

The DataStudio software, Workbooks, and Configuration Files should be installed before using this quick start guide.

Step 1   Plug in the USB Link and the probe or sensor needed for your lab.
Step 2   Choose the workbook or configuration file for your lab in the PASPortal window. (See below.)

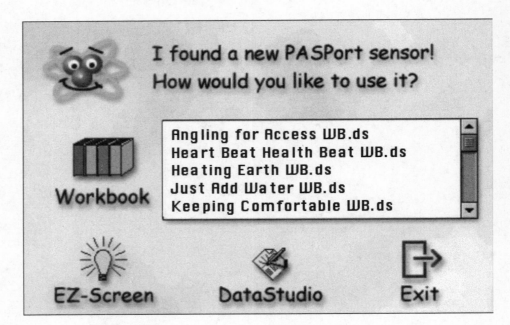

You can obtain a free 90-day trial version of DataStudio to review each of the enclosed PASCO electronic workbooks. Simply go to the PASCO web site at www.pasco.com and download the trial software.

Introducing Xplorer, PASCO's new data logger.

The **Xplorer** is the new data logger from PASCO scientific. *Easy to use and versatile,* the **Xplorer** is another educational tool from our e-measure line.

The **Xplorer** has *plug-and-play capability*—plug in a sensor, and you're recording and displaying data! The **Xplorer** can be used with all PASPORT sensors.

The **Xplorer** can be used as a *data logger without a computer* for stand-alone operation. Expand the logging flexibility back in the classroom, by plugging the **Xplorer** into the USB port of your PC or Macintosh. Extend your teaching and learning environment using DataStudio, PASCO's powerful data collection and analysis software.

The **Xplorer** encourages student creativity by allowing them to operate beyond the limits of the theoretical. The **Xplorer** lets students capture and display phenomena in real time!

Your PASPORT to science discovery.

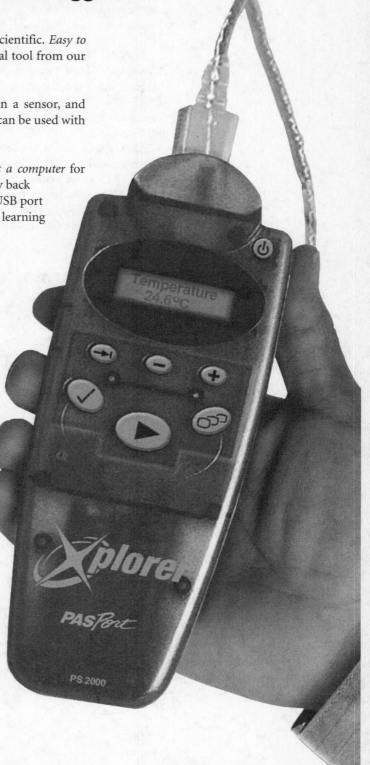

The Science Explorer Bundle includes the PASPORT equipment needed to measure heart rate, temperature, conductivity and force. Equipped with the latest in technology, the new PASPORT Xplorer hand-held data logger which displays all measurements and units in the field…in real time! The bundle includes the following equipment.

- **1 PASPORT Xplorer** (PS-2000) See the Xplorer Fact Sheet on page vii.
- **1 PASPORT Heart Rate Sensor** (PS-2105) Clip for detecting pulse. LED flashes on unit to indicate pulse.
- **1 PASPORT Temperature Sensor** (PS-2101) Comes with a removable Teflon cover for use with harsh liquids or chemical solutions. −10 to 110°C, 14-cm probe
- **1 PASPORT Conductivity Sensor** (PS-2116) 3 ranges covering 0–200,000 µS/cm, resolution 10µS/cm or better
- **1 PASPORT Force Sensor** (PS-2104) −50 to 50 N range, finger holes for hand-held use, clamp for mount to rods, tare button to zero, overload protected
- **1 PASPORT USB Link** (PS-2100) For connecting PASPORT sensors to the USB port on the computer

Ordering Information

DataStudio software must be ordered separately.

DataStudio Software—Single User	(CI-6870A)	$99.00
Data Studio Software—Site License	(CI-6871B)	$349.00
The Science Explorer Bundle:	(PS-2735)	$599.00
PASPORT Conductivity Sensor	(PD-2116)	$155.00
PASPORT Heart Rate Sensor	(PD-2105)	$ 79.00
PASPORT Force Sensor	(PS-2102)	$109.00
PASPORT Temperature Sensor	(PS-2101)	$ 49.00
USB Link	(PS-2100)	$ 59.00
Xplorer	(PS-2000)	$149.00
USB 4-port Hub	(PS-2501)	$ 38.00

Texas Instruments Hardware and Software Information

Let your students discover science in the world around them by helping them develop hypotheses, complete experiments, and form conclusions.

The CBL 2™

The CBL 2 provides the easiest, most accessible way for students to collect and analyze real-world data.

- The CBL 2 is easy to use. (Some products take a lot of time and effort to set up and learn to use. Not so with the CBL 2.)
- Built-in software (DataMate) is transferred to your calculator with the push of a single button. Start collecting data right away, or quickly set up the CBL 2 for more sophisticated applications.

Collect data with one of the more than 40 available sensors from Vernier Software & Technology. The range of sensors available with the CBL 2 allows you and your students to try a wide variety of physics investigations. More detailed features about the CBL 2 are available in the User's Guide found on the CD-ROM in this Lab Manual. Simply launch the probeware file on the CD-ROM and click on Texas Instruments. There is also up-to-date information at the product section of the TI Web site.

General TI Information

Contact the TI Customer Support Line to order products, before returning a product for service, or if you have general questions about using a product.

Call: 1-800-TI-CARES (800-842-2737)

Monday–Thursday: 8:00 A.M. to 7:00 P.M. CST

Friday: 10:00 A.M. to 7:00 P.M. CST

E-mail: ti-cares@ti.com

Write: Texas Instruments
Customer Support Line
PO Box 650311, MS 3962
Dallas, TX 75265

Technical Assistance

The TI Technical Assistance Group is trained to answer your technical questions about TI calculators, software, and accessories.

Call: 972-917-8324 (This is not a toll-free number)

Monday–Thursday: 8:00 A.M. to 4:30 P.M. CST

Friday: 10:00 A.M. to 4:30 P.M. CST

E-mail: ti-cares@ti.com

Write: Texas Instruments
Technical Assistance Group
PO Box 650311, MS 3962
Dallas, TX 75265

Using DataMate

Vernier's DataMate program for TI Graphing Calculators is used to collect, examine, analyze, and graph data. DataMate is a group of programs that runs collectively as a single program or application. The TI-83 Plus shows DataMate as a single application (or APP). The other calculators list all of the sub-programs, but you will always choose the main program, DataMate.

Use the link cable to connect the LabPro or CBL 2 to the TI Graphing Calculator. Firmly press in the cable ends. Turn on the calculator. Follow these steps to start the DataMate program on your calculator:

TI-73 or TI-83 Calculators
Press PRGM, and then press the calculator key for the *number* that precedes DataMate (usually 1). Press ENTER and wait for the main screen to load.

TI-83 Plus Calculators
Press APPS, and then press the calculator key for the *number* that precedes the DataMate program. Wait for the main screen to load.

TI-86 Calculators
Press PRGM, press F1 to select <NAMES>, and press the menu key that represents DataMate. (<DATAM> is usually F1.)Press ENTER, and wait for the main screen to load.

TI-89, TI-92, or TI-92 Plus Calculators
Press 2nd [VAR-LINK]. Use the cursor pad to scroll down to "DataMate", then press ENTER. Press) to complete the open parenthesis that follows "DataMate" on the entry line, and press ENTER. Wait for the main screen to load.

For full details about program features and calibration, see the DataMate guide on the Texas Instruments screen of the Probeware CD-ROM.

Transferring a Calculator Graph to a Computer for Printing

Many labs in the Probeware Lab Manual have an optional step to print a graph. To print a graph you need a TI-Graph Link cable and the version of TI-Graph Link software appropriate for your computer and calculator type. Before doing a lab that requires printing, you may want to show your students how to print graphs.

TI-GRAPH LINK Windows Version

TI-73, TI-83, TI-83 Plus, and TI-86 Calculators
- Connect the TI-Graph Link cable to the serial port of the Windows computer and to the port on the bottom edge of the calculator.
- The graph that you want to print should be displayed on the calculator screen.
- Using the TI-Graph Link software, choose Get Screen from the Link menu.
- Choose the size of graph you want to print from the pop-up menu.
- Click on Get Screen.
- Click on Print and then click on OK.
- Click on Done when you are finished printing.

TI-89, TI-92, and TI-92 Plus Calculators
- Connect the TI-Graph Link cable to the serial port of the Windows computer and to the port on the bottom edge of the TI-89, or the port on the top-left edge of the TI-92 and TI-92 Plus.
- The graph that you want to print should be displayed on the calculator screen.
- Using the TI-Graph Link software, choose Get Screen from the Link menu.
- Click on the Get Screen button.
- Click on Print.
- Click on OK.
- Once the graph is printed, click on Done.

TI-GRAPH LINK 2.x, Macintosh Version

TI-GRAPH LINK 2.x software for Macintosh allows you to set a number of preferences. (See the Startup item in Preferences in the Edit menu.) The instructions that follow assume that no windows or connections are opened at the time Graph Link is launched, and that your Graph Link cable is connected using the modem port. Depending on how your preferences are set, you may see open windows; if a connection to the calculator is already established, skip the two connection steps. (*NOTE:* These instructions refer only to version 2.x of TI-Graph Link for Macintosh. Earlier versions may be used, but the procedure is quite different.)

All Calculators

- Connect the TI-Graph Link cable to the serial port of the Macintosh and to the port on the bottom edge of the TI-73, TI-83, TI-83 Plus, TI-86, TI-89 or the top-left edge of the TI-92 and TI-92 Plus.
- The graph that you want to print should be displayed on the calculator screen.
- Make sure the TI-Graph Link cable is connected to the calculator and the calculator is turned on.
- Start up TI-Graph Link 2 by double-clicking on the TI-Graph Link 2 icon.
- Select TI-73, 83, 83 Plus, 86, 89, 92, or 92 Plus from the Connection Menu.
- Select Get Screen from the Window menu or double-click on the screen object in the calculator window. A new window called "Screen" will appear displaying the graph from the calculator screen.
- Select Print from the File menu. Click on Print in the Print window.

Vernier Hardware and Software

Vernier Software & Technology has been serving science teachers since 1981. The first products were developed for Apple II™ computers and designed to take the drudgery out of making graphs, measuring temperature, and timing moving objects. Since then, Vernier has developed a full line of data collection products for Macintosh computers, PC computers, and Texas Instruments graphing calculators. Over 40 different sensors are available. Auto-ID sensors and user-friendly software simplify data collection and analysis. A generous site license policy and reasonably priced sensors make data collection technology affordable.

You will find valuable information on the CD-ROM that comes with this Probeware Lab Manual. Simply insert the CD-ROM, open the probeware file, and click on the Vernier button.

Contact Information

For customer support, product information, and current prices, please contact

> Vernier Software & Technology
> 13979 SW Millikan Way
> Beaverton, OR 97005-2886

> **Phone:**   (503) 277-2299
> **Fax:**   (503) 277-2440
> **Web site:**   www.vernier.com
> **E-mail:**   info@vernier.com

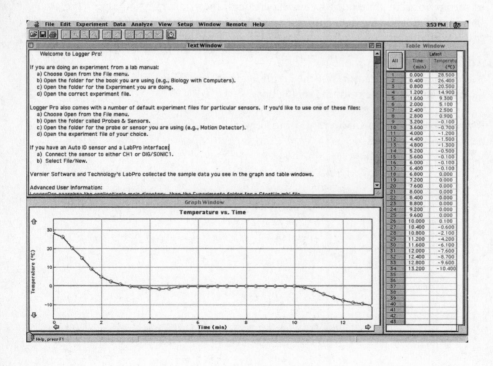

Logger *Pro* Quick Start

Before using the labs in this Probeware Lab Manual, you must first install the Logger *Pro* configuration files by following the instructions on the attached CD-ROM. The CD-ROM provides only the configuration files; the Logger *Pro* software is sold separately by Vernier.

After the configuration files are installed, follow these steps:

Attach interface and sensor

- Attach the LabPro or CBL 2™ Interface to the computer using the supplied cable. On the Macintosh you can use any serial port, including the modem and printer ports. On the PC you can use any of the COM 1, 2, 3 or 4 serial ports. LabPro users can also use the USB port and cable on a USB-equipped PC or Macintosh.
- Attach the power adapter to the interface and to a source of 115-V AC.
- Attach a sensor to the interface.

Start up Logger *Pro*

Locate the Logger *Pro* icon and double-click on it, or use the Start menu (Windows 95/98/NT).

Configure Logger *Pro* for your sensor

Choose Open from the File menu, and choose an experiment file from the *Science Explorer* folder. There is more than one file for some labs; choose the file that matches your particular hardware. Calibration is automatically loaded with the experiment file.

Collect data

At the appropriate time during your experiment, click on [▶ Collect]. Logger *Pro* should begin collecting data and, if a graph is present, plotting data in the graph window.

Adjust graph

You can adjust most features of the graph by double-clicking on the graph and making changes in the resulting dialog box.

If you need more information for using Logger *Pro*, refer to the extensive online help or User's Manual.

Materials List

You will need the following materials for all nine labs.

PASCO

Computer (Macintosh with System 8.6 or higher or Windows 98 or 2000) with
    USB port
1 USB Link per sensor used
DataStudio Software
PASPORT Sensors as indicated below
(Sunny Rays and Angles also may require a USB hub)

Vernier

Computer (Macintosh with System 7.6 through 9.x or Windows 95, 98, 2000, or
    NT) with serial port or PS2 port
LabPro Interface or CBL 2™
Logger *Pro* software
Vernier Sensors as indicated below

Texas Instruments

TI graphing calculator
CBL 2 or LabPro Interface
DataMate Software
TI-Graph Link cable and software to transfer DataMate to the CBL 2
    or LabPro unit
Vernier Sensors as indicated below

In addition, you will need the following materials for each lab.

Angling for Access
force sensor
board, at least 10 cm wide and 50 cm long
wooden block with eye-hook
metric ruler
marker
4 books, about 2 cm thick

Heart Beat, Health Beat
heart rate monitor

Heating Earth's Surface
2 temperature sensors
ring stand and ring clamp
2 beakers, 400 mL
sand, 300 mL
water, 300 mL
lamp with 100-W bulb
string
graph paper
metric ruler

Materials List *(continued)*

Just Add Water
temperature sensors
4 plastic foam cups
balance/scale
hot tap water
pencil
scissors
beaker of water kept in an ice bath

Keeping Comfortable
temperature sensor
hot water
ice water
beakers
containers and lids made of paper, plastic foam, plastic, glass, and metal

Melting Ice
temperature sensor
2 plastic cups, about 200 mL each
ice cubes, about 2 cm on each side
warm water, about 40°C to 45°C
room temperature water, about 20°C to 25°C

Shedding Light on Chemical Bonds
conductivity sensor
small beaker
plastic spoon
sodium chloride
100-mL graduated cylinder
additional substances supplied by your teacher

Sticky Sneakers
force sensor
three or more different types of sneakers
mass set(s)
tape
3 large paper clips

Sunny Rays and Angles
temperature sensors
books
pencil
scissors
ruler
protractor
clear tape
100-W incandescent lamp
black construction paper

Angling for Access

You and your friends have volunteered to help build a wheelchair-access ramp for the local public library. The design of the ramp has not been decided upon yet, so you need to build a model inclined plane. The model will help you determine what the steepness of the ramp should be.

◆ **Problem**   How does the steepness of a wheelchair-access ramp affect its usefulness?

◆ **Skills Focus**   making models, measuring, calculating

◆ **Materials**

PASPORT Force Sensor
USB Link
board, at least 10 cm wide and 50 cm long
wooden block with eye-hook
metric ruler
marker
4 books, about 2 cm thick

◆ **Procedure**

1. Plug the USB Link into the computer's USB port.

2. Plug the force sensor into the USB Link.

This will automatically launch the PASPORTAL window.

Angling for Access *(continued)*

3. Choose the appropriate electronic workbook *or* the proper DataStudio configuration file.

➤ If you are going to use the PASCO electronic workbook specifically designed for this activity, then simply click on the workbook entitled

Angling for Access WB.ds

and go!

➤ If you are *not* using an electronic workbook, then click on the DataStudio icon and then from the menu bar, select File > Open Activity. Next, choose

Angling for Access CF.ds

and proceed with the following instructions.

4. To zero the force sensor, press the button labeled ZERO.

5. Preview the following steps that describe how you can construct and use a ra____ ____ie data table to record your data.

6. The output force on an inclined plane is equal to the weight of the object. Click on ▶ Start .

Lift the block with the force sensor to measure its weight. Record this value in the data table as the Output Force. Click on ■ Stop .

7. Make a mark on the side of the board about 3 cm from one end. Measure the length from the other end of the board to the mark, and record it in the data table as the Length of Incline.

8. Place one end of the board on top of a book. The mark you made on the board should be even with the edge of the book.

9. Measure the vertical distance in centimeters from the top of the table to where the underside of the incline touches the book. Record this value in the data table as the Height of Incline.

10. Lay the block on its largest side. Click on the Start button and use the force sensor to pull the block straight up the incline at a slow, steady speed. Be sure to hold the force sensor parallel to the incline, as shown in the diagram. The force sensor measures your pulling force and shows it on a graph display. Click on the Stop button to end the trial.

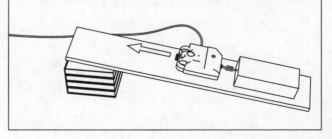

Angling for Access *(continued)*

11. Predict how your results will change if you repeat the investigation using two, three, and four books. Test your predictions.

12. For each trial, find the Input Force and record it in the data table. Use your data to calculate the ideal mechanical advantage and the actual mechanical advantage. Record the calculations in your data table. *NOTE:* The Input Force is the average of the pulling force you measured with the force sensor. You can use the built-in analysis tools in the DataStudio software to find the average pulling force.

$$\text{Ideal Mechanical Advantage} = \frac{\text{Length of Incline}}{\text{Height of Incline}}$$

$$\text{Actual Mechanical Advantage} = \frac{\text{Weight of Block}}{\text{Input Force}}$$

◆ In the graph tool bar, click on the Data button and select the trial.
   _____ nouse to click-and-draw a rectangle around the part
   _____ rs where you were pulling with the force sensor.

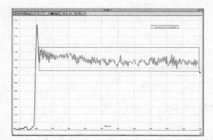

◆ In the tool bar, click on the Statistics button Σ ▼ and select Mean.
◆ In the graph, look at the Legend Box to find the mean. Record this as the Input Force in the data table.

◆ Data Table

Number of Books	Output Force (N)	Length of Incline (cm)	Height of Incline (cm)	Input Force (N)	Ideal Mechanical Advantage	Actual Mechanical Advantage
1						
2						
3						
4						

© Prentice-Hall, Inc.

PASCO

Angling for Access *(continued)*

◆ Analyze and Conclude

Write your answers on the back of this sheet or on a separate sheet of paper.

1. How did the ideal mechanical advantage and the actual mechanical advantage compare each time you repeated the experiment? Explain your answer.

2. Why do you write ideal and actual mechanical advantage without units?

3. What happens to the mechanical advantage as the inclined plane gets steeper? On the basis of this fact alone, which of the four inclined planes models the best steepness for a wheelchair-access ramp?

4. What other factors, besides mechanical advantage, should you consider when deciding on the steepness of the ramp?

5. **Apply** Suppose the door of the local public library is 2 m above the ground and the distance from the door to the parking lot is 15 m. How would these conditions affect your decision about how steep to make the ramp?

◆ Getting Involved

Find actual ramps that provide access for people with disabilities. Measure the heights and lengths of these ramps and calculate their ideal mechanical advantages. Find out what the requirements are for access ramps in your area. Should your ramp be made of a particular material? Should it level off before it reaches the door? How wide should it be? How does it provide water drainage?

© Prentice-Hall, Inc.

PASCO version | **SKILLS LAB**

Measuring

PASCO

Heart Beat, Health Beat

◆ **Problem** How does physical activity affect your pulse rate?

◆ **Materials**

USB Link
PASPORT Heart Rate Sensor

◆ **Procedure**  *Review the safety guidelines in Appendix A.*

1. Predict how your pulse rate will change as you go from resting to being active, then back to resting again.

2. Plug the USB Link into the computer's USB port.

3. Plug the heart rate sensor into the USB Link.

This will automatically launch the PASPORTAL window.

> I found a new PASPort sensor! How would you like to use it?
>
> Heart Beat Health Beat WB.ds
>
> Workbook
>
> EZ-Screen DataStudio Exit

Heart Beat, Health Beat *(continued)*

4. Choose the appropriate electronic workbook *or* the proper DataStudio configuration file.

> ➤ If you are going to use the PASCO electronic workbook specifically designed for this activity, then simply click on the workbook entitled

Heart Beat Health Beat WB.ds

and go!

> ➤ If you are *not* using an electronic workbook, then click on the DataStudio icon and then from the menu bar, select File > Open Activity. Next, choose

Heart Beat Health Beat CF.ds

and proceed with the following instructions.

5. Plug the heart rate sensor clip into the heart rate sensor. Place the heart rate sensor clip on your earlobe or on the tip of a finger.

6. Work with a partner for the rest of this lab. Begin by determining your resting pulse rate. Sit still and breathe normally while your partner clicks on ► Start .

After 60 seconds have elapsed, your partner will click on ■ Stop .

7. In the graph, use the Smart Tool to find your pulse rate in beats per minute (beats/min). Click on the Smart Tool, [icon], in the tool bar and position the tool in the middle of a section of the graph that is mostly flat. The second number in the parentheses next to the Smart Tool is your pulse rate in beats/min. Record it in your data table.

CAUTION: *Do not complete the rest of these procedures if there is any medical reason why you should avoid physical activities.*

8. Unclip the heart rate sensor.

9. Walk in place for one minute while your partner times you. Stop walking, sit down and immediately clip the heart rate sensor on your earlobe or on the tip of a finger. Check your pulse rate for one minute. Use the Smart Tool to find your pulse rate and record the number in your data table.

10. Unclip the heart rate sensor.

11. Run in place for one minute. Immediately clip the heart rate sensor on your earlobe or on the tip of a finger. Check your pulse rate again, and record the result.

12. Then, sit down and have your partner time you as you rest for one minute. Take your pulse rate again. Record that number in the data table.

13. Have your partner time you as you rest for 3 more minutes. Then, take your pulse rate again and record it in the data table.

PASCO

Heart Beat, Health Beat *(continued)*

◆ Data Table

Activity	Pulse Rate
Resting	
Walking	
Running	
Resting after Exercise	
(1 min) Resting after Exercise	
(3+ min) Resting after Exercise	

◆ Analyze and Conclude

Write your answers on the back of this sheet or on a separate sheet of paper.

1. Use the data you obtained to create a bar graph of your pulse rate under the different conditions you tested.
2. What conclusion can you draw about the relationship between physical activity and a person's pulse rate?
3. What happens to the pulse rate when the physical activity has stopped?
4. What can you infer about the heartbeat when the pulse rate increases?
5. **Think About It** Do you think the pulse measurements you made are completely accurate? Why or why not? How could you improve the accuracy of your measurements?

◆ Design an Experiment

Do the resting pulse rates of adults, teens, and young children differ? Write a plan to answer this question. Obtain your teacher's permission before carrying out your plan.

PASCO

PASCO version   **SKILLS LAB**

Developing Hypotheses

PASCO

Heating Earth's Surface

In this lab, you will develop and test a hypothesis about how quickly different materials absorb radiation.

◆ **Problem** How do the heating and cooling rates of sand and water compare?

◆ **Materials**

2 PASPORT Temperature Sensors   water, 300 mL
2 USB Links   lamp with 100-W bulb
ring stand and ring clamp   string
2 beakers, 400 mL   graph paper
sand, 300 mL   metric ruler

◆ **Procedure**  *Review the safety guidelines in Appendix A.*

1. Plug the USB Link into the computer's USB port.

2. Plug the temperature sensor into the USB Link.

This will automatically launch the PASPORTAL window.

I found a new PASPort sensor!
How would you like to use it?

Heating Earths Surface WB.ds

Workbook

EZ-Screen   DataStudio   Exit

Heating Earth's Surface *(continued)*

3. Choose the appropriate electronic workbook *or* DataStudio configuration file.

   ➤ If you are using the PASCO electronic workbook specifically designed for this activity, then simply click on the workbook entitled

   Heating Earths Surface WB.ds

   and go!

   ➤ If you are using the PASCO configuration file, then click on the file entitled

   Heating Earths Surface *CF.ds*

   and proceed with the following instructions.

4. Do you think sand or water will heat up faster? Record your hypothesis on a separate sheet of paper. Explain what information you used to form your hypothesis. Next, which material do you think will cool off more quickly? Record your hypothesis. Again, give reasons why you think your hypothesis is correct.

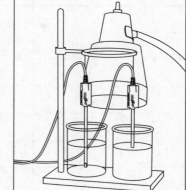

5. Use the data table to record your data.

6. Fill one beaker with 300 mL of dry sand.

7. Fill the second beaker with 300 mL of water at room temperature.

8. Arrange the beakers beneath the ring stand.

9. Place one temperature sensor in each beaker.

10. Suspend the temperature sensors from the ring stand with string. This will hold the sensors in place so they do not fall.

11. Adjust the height of the ring stand so that the tip of each sensor is covered by about 1 cm of sand or water in a beaker.

12. Position the lamp so that it is about 20 cm above the sand and water. There should be no more than 8 cm between the beakers. **CAUTION:** *Be careful not to splash water onto the hot light bulb.*

13. Measure the rate at which each substance warms up. Click on ▶ Start . Record the beginning temperatures of the sand and water in your data table. (They should be about the same.)

14. Turn on the lamp. The temperature sensors will record the temperature of the sand and water once every minute. Read the temperature of the sand and water every minute for 15 minutes. Record the temperatures in the Light On column in the data table.

Heating Earth's Surface *(continued)*

15. Now measure the rate at which each substance cools down. Turn the light off. Record the temperature of the sand and water once every minute for another 15 minutes. Record the temperatures in the Light Off column (16–30 minutes).

16. Click on ■ Stop .

◆ **Data Table**

Temperature with Light On (°C)			Temperature with Light Off (°C)		
Time (min)	Sand	Water	Time (min)	Sand	Water
Start			16		
1			17		
2			18		
3			19		
4			20		
5			21		
6			22		
7			23		
8			24		
9			25		
10			26		
11			27		
12			28		
13			29		
14			30		
15					

Heating Earth's Surface *(continued)*

◆ Analyze ıd Conclude

Write your answers on a separa   eet of paper.

1. Use the Note Tool $\boxed{A}$ to label your runs "Sand" and "Water" in the graph.

2. In the graph, use the Smart Tool $\boxed{}$ to find the beginning and final temperatures for the water and the sand. (*NOTE:* Select one of the runs of data. Click on the Smart Tool button in the graph tool bar. Move the Smart Tool to the beginning of the run of data. The second number next to the Smart Tool is the beginning temperature. Move the Smart Tool to the end of the data to find the final temperature. Repeat for the other run of data.) Use your data to calculate the total change in temperature for each material.

3. Based on your data, which material had the greater increase in temperature?

4. What can you conclude about which material absorbed heat faster? How do your results compare with your hypothesis?

5. Review your data again. In 15 minutes, which material cooled faster?

6. How do these results compare to your second hypothesis?

7. **Think About It** If your results did not support either of your hypotheses, why do you think the results differed from what you expected?

8. **Apply** Based on your results, which do you think will heat up more quickly on a sunny day, the water in a lake or the sand surrounding it? Which will cool off more quickly after dark?

◆ More to Explore

Do you think all solid materials heat up as fast as sand? For example, consider gravel, crushed stone, or different types of soil. Write a hypothesis about their heating rates. With the approval and supervision of your teacher, develop a procedure to test your hypothesis. Was your hypothesis correct?

PASCO

PASCO

PASCO version   **SKILLS LAB**

Interpreting Data

Just Add Water

If you add hot water to cold water, what will happen? In this lab, you'll make a device that measures changes in thermal energy. It is called a calorimeter. You will use the skill of interpreting data to calculate the thermal energy transferred.

◆ **Problem** When hot and cold water are mixed, how much thermal energy is transferred from the hot water to the cold water?

◆ **Materials**

2 USB Links   hot tap water
2 PASPORT Temperature Sensors   pencil
4 plastic foam cups   scissors
balance   beaker of water kept in an ice bath

Making a Calorimeter

A. Label a plastic foam cup with the letter C ("C" stands for cold water).

B. Cut 2 to 3 cm from the top of a second plastic foam cup. Invert the second cup inside the first. Label the cover with a C also. The cup and cover are your cold-water calorimeter.

C. Using a pencil, poke a hole in the cover large enough for a temperature sensor to fit snugly.

D. Repeat Steps A, B, and C with two other plastic foam cups. This time, label both cup and cover with an H. This is your hot-water calorimeter.

◆ **Procedure** *Review the safety guidelines in Appendix A.*

1. Predict how the amount of thermal energy lost by hot water will be related to the amount of thermal energy gained by cold water.

2. Plug the USB Link into the computer's USB port.

© Prentice-Hall, Inc.

JUST ADD WATER *(continued)*

nto the USB Link.

This will automatically launch the PASPORTAL window.

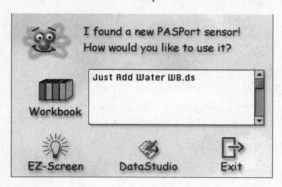

4. Choose the appropriate electronic workbook *or* the proper DataStudio configuration file.

   ➤ If you are going to use the PASCO electronic workbook specifically designed for this activity, then simply click on the workbook entitled

   Just Add Water WB.ds

   and go!

   ➤ If you are *not* using an electronic workbook, then click on the DataStudio icon and then from the menu bar, select File > Open Activity. Next, choose

   Just Add Water CF.ds

   and proceed with the following instructions.

5. Use the data table to record all data.

6. Follow the instructions in the box to make two calorimeters. Find the mass of each empty calorimeter (including the cover) on a balance and record each mass in your data table.

7. From a beaker of water that has been sitting in an ice bath, add water (no ice cubes) to the cold-water calorimeter. Fill it about one-third full. Put the cover on, find the total mass, and record the mass in your data table.

8. Add hot tap water to the hot-water calorimeter. Fill it about one-third full. **CAUTION:** *Hot tap water can cause burns.*

9. Put the cover on, find the total mass, and record the mass in your data table.

JUST ADD WATER *(continued)*

10. Calculate the mass of the water in each calorimeter. Record the results in your data table.

11. Put the temperature sensors through the holes in the covers of both calorimeters. Wait one minute so the two sensors will be at the same temperature before you use them.

12. Click on ▶ Start .

13. Let the temperature sensors record the temperature of the water in the two calorimeters for 20 seconds. Then remove both temperature sensors and covers. Pour the water from the cold-water calorimeter into the hot-water calorimeter. Put the cover back on the hot-water calorimeter and insert a temperature sensor (it doesn't matter which one). Wait until the temperature stops dropping and stabilizes.

14. Click on ■ Stop .

15. Use the Smart tool, [xy icon], to find the initial and final temperature of the water in each calorimeter, as well as the final temperature of the combined water. Record your data in the data table.

◆ Data Table

	Mass of Empty Cup (g)	Mass of Cup and Water (g)	Mass of Water (g)	Starting Temp. (°C)	Final Temp. (°C)	Change in Temp. (°C)
Cold-Water Calorimeter						
Hot-Water Calorimeter						

JUST ADD WATER *(continued)*

◆ Analyze and Conclude

Write your answers on the back of this sheet or on a separate sheet of paper.

1. What is the temperature change of the cold water? Record your answer in the data table.

2. What is the temperature change of the hot water? Record your answer in the data table.

3. Calculate the amount of thermal energy that enters the cold water by using the formula for the transfer of thermal energy. The specific heat of water is 4.18 J/(g•K), so you use the following formula.

   Thermal energy transferred = 4.18 J/(g•K) × Mass of cold water × Temperature change of cold water. Remember that 1°C is equal to 1 K.

4. Now use the formula to calculate the thermal energy leaving the hot water.

5. What unit should you use for your results for Questions 3 and 4?

6. Was your prediction from Step 1 confirmed? How do you know?

7. **Think About It** What sources of error might have affected your results? How could the lab be redesigned in order to reduce the errors?

◆ Design an Experiment

How would your results be affected if you started with much more hot water than cold? If you used more cold water than hot? Make a prediction. Then design a procedure to test your prediction. Get your teacher's approval, and try your new procedure.

PASCO

PASCO version   **SKILLS LAB**

Designing Experiments

Keeping Comfortable

Two ways to use less energy are to keep heat out of your home when the weather is hot, and to keep heat in when the weather is cold. In this lab, you will design an experiment to compare how well different materials do this.

◆ Problem   How well do different materials stop heat transfer?

◆ Suggested Materials

USB Link
PASPORT Temperature Sensor
hot water
ice water
beakers
containers and lids made of paper, plastic foam, plastic, glass, and metal

◆ Design a Plan   *Review the safety guidelines in Appendix A.*

1. Plug the USB Link into the computer's USB port.

2. Plug the temperature sensor into the USB Link.

This will automatically launch the PASPORTAL window.

> I found a new PASPort sensor!
> How would you like to use it?
>
> **Workbook**   Keeping Comfortable WB.ds
>
> EZ-Screen   DataStudio   Exit

KEEPING COMFORTABLE *(continued)*

3. Choose the appropriate electronic workbook *or* DataStudio configuration file.

   ➤ If you are using the PASCO electronic workbook specifically designed for this activity, then simply click on the workbook entitled

   Keeping Comfortable WB.ds

   and go!

   ➤ If you are using the PASCO configuration file, then click the file entitled

   Keeping Comfortable CF.ds

   and proceed with the following instructions.

◆ **Part 1 Measuring Temperature Changes**

4. Use a pencil to poke a hole in the lid of a paper cup. Fill the cup about halfway with cold water.

5. Put the lid on the cup. Insert the temperature sensor into the water through the hole.

6. Click on ▶ Start .

7. Watch the display of temperature. When the temperature stops dropping, place the cup in a beaker. Add hot water to the beaker until the water level is about 1 cm below the lid.

8. When the water temperature has increased by 5°C, click on ■ Stop .

9. Use the Smart Tool ⬚ to find the time it took for the temperature to increase by 1°C. Use this value as a measure of the effectiveness of the paper cup in preventing heat transfer.

PASCO

KEEPING COMFORTABLE *(continued)*

◆ **Part 2 Comparing Materials**

10. Use the ideas from Part 1 to design a controlled experiment to rank the effectiveness of different materials in preventing heat transfer.

    Hint: For instance you may want to monitor the temperature from run to run so that it remains constant.

11. Use these questions to help you plan your experiment:
    ◆ What hypothesis will you test?
    ◆ Which materials do you predict will be the best and worst at preventing heat transfer?
    ◆ How will you define these terms?
    ◆ What will your manipulated variable be?
    ◆ What will your responding variable be?
    ◆ What variables do you need to control?
    ◆ How will you control them?
    ◆ What step-by-step procedures will you use?
    ◆ What kind of data table will you use?

12. After your teacher has reviewed your plans, make any necessary changes in your design. Then perform your experiment.

◆ **Analyze and Conclude**

1. In Part 1, what was the starting temperature of the hot water? What was the starting temperature of the cold water? In which direction did the heat flow? How do you know?

2. If the materials in Part 1 are used to represent your home in very hot weather, which material would represent the rooms in your home? Which would represent the outdoor weather? Which would represent the walls of the building?

3. Which material was most effective at blocking the transfer of heat? Which was the least effective? Explain.

4. **Think About It** Would experiments similar to this one provide you with enough information to choose materials to build a home? Explain.

◆ **More to Explore**

Create a plan to compare how well the materials would work if the hot water were inside the cup and the cold water were outside. With your teacher's permission, carry out your plan.

© Prentice-Hall, Inc.

KEEPING COMFORTABLE *(continued)*

EXPERIMENT PLAN

Write your experiment plan below. If you need more room, use a separate sheet of paper.

◆ **Hypothesis**

_____

_____

◆ **Materials**

_____

_____

_____

_____

◆ **Procedure**

_____

_____

_____

_____

_____

_____

_____

_____

_____

_____

_____

_____

◆ **Data Table**

PASCO

Melting Ice

In this experiment, you will measure temperature as you explore the melting of ice.

◆ **Problem**   How does the temperature of the surroundings affect the rate
at which ice melts?

◆ **Materials**

USB Link
PASPORT Temperature Sensor
plastic cup, about 200 mL
ice cubes, about 2 cm on each side
warm water, about 40°C to 45°C
water at room temperature, about 20°C

◆ **Procedure**   🤿   *Review the safety guidelines in Appendix A.*

1. Plug the USB Link into the computer's USB port.

2. Plug the temperature sensor into the USB Link.

This will automatically launch the PASPORTAL window.

> 🕷️ **I found a new PASPort sensor!**
> **How would you like to use it?**
>
> 📚 **Workbook** | Melting Ice WB.ds |
>
> 💡 EZ-Screen   🗒️ DataStudio   ➡️ Exit

MELTING ICE *(continued)*

3. Choose the appropriate electronic workbook *or* DataStudio configuration file.

   ➤ If you are going to use the PASCO electronic workbook specifically designed for this activity, then simply click on the workbook entitled

   Melting Ice WB.ds

   and go!

   ➤ If you are using the PASCO configuration file, then click the file entitled

   Melting Ice CF.ds

   and proceed with the following instructions.

4. Read Steps 5–15. Based on your own experience, predict which ice cube will melt faster.

5. Fill a cup halfway with warm water (about 40°C to 45°C).

6. Obtain an ice cube that is as close to the same size as the other available ice cu   sible.

7. Place the temperature sensor in the warm water.

8. Click on ► Start .

9. When the temperature is stable, add an ice cube to the cup.

10. Gently stir the solution with the temperature sensor.

11. When the ice cube is completely melted, click on ■ Stop .

12. Click on the Scale to Fit button ⬈ to obtain the best view of the graph.

13. Use the Smart Tool ⊞ to find the beginning temperature, the time for the ice cube to melt, and the final temperature. Record the values in the table.

14. Empty the water from the cup, and fill the cup halfway with water at room temperature.

15. Repeat Steps 6–14 for the room temperature water.

PASCO

MELTING ICE *(continued)*

◆ Data Table

	Beginning Temperature (°C)	Time to Melt (s)	Final Temperature (°C)
Cup 1			
Cup 2			

◆ Analyze and Conclude

Write your answers on the back of this sheet or on a separate sheet of paper.

1. Was your prediction in Step 4 supported by the results of the experiment? Explain why or why not.

2. In which cup did the water temperature change the most? Explain this result.

3. When the ice melted, its molecules gained enough energy to overcome the forces holding them together as solid ice. What is the source of that energy?

4. **Think About It** How well could you time the exact moment that each ice cube completely melted? How might errors in measurements affect your conclusions?

◆ Design an Experiment

When a lake freezes in winter, only the top turns to ice. Design an experiment to model the melting of a frozen lake during the spring. With your teacher's approval, carry out your experiment. Be prepared to share your results with the class.

Shedding Light on Chemical Bonds

Electricity is the flow of electric current. In this lab, you will interpret data about which compounds conduct electricity in order to determine the nature of their bonds.

◆ **Problem**   How can you use a conductivity tester to determine whether a compound contains ionic or covalent bonds?

◆ **Materials**

USB Link
PASPORT Conductivity Sensor
small beaker
small plastic spoon
sodium chloride
100-mL graduated cylinder
additional substances supplied by your teacher

◆ **Procedure**   *Review the safety guidelines in Appendix A.*

                        mputer's USB port.

                        nto the USB Link.

This will automatically launch the PASPORTAL window.

I found a new PASPort sensor!
How would you like to use it?

Shedding Light on Ch WB.ds

Workbook

EZ-Screen   DataStudio   Exit

SHEDDING LIGHT ON CHEMICAL BONDS (continued)

3. Choose the appropriate electronic workbook *or* the proper DataStudio configuration file.

   ➤ If you are going to use the PASCO electronic workbook specifically designed for this activity, then simply click on the workbook entitled

   Shedding Light on Chemical Bonds WB.ds

   and go!

   ➤ If you are *not* using an electronic workbook, then click on the DataStudio icon and then from the menu bar, select File > Open Activity. Next, choose

   Shedding Light on Chemical Bonds CF.ds

   and proceed with the following instructions.

4. Use the data table to record your data.

5. Pour about 50 mL _____ nto a beaker. Place the conductivity sensor in the water.

6. Click on the Start button ▶ Start .

7. Look at the digits display to find the value measured by the conductivity sensor. Record the water's conductivity in your data table.

8. Remove the conductivity sensor and add a small spoonful of sodium chloride to the water in the beaker. Stir the mixture with the spoon until the salt is dissolved.

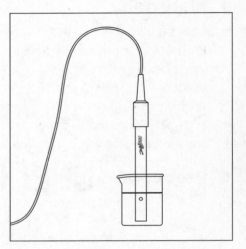

9. Repeat the conductivity measurement and record the conductivity in your data table.

10. Click on the Stop button ■ Stop .

11. Dispose of the sodium chloride and water as instructed. Carefully rinse the beaker, spoon, and conductivity sensor with clear water.

12. Repeat the procedure to measure the conductivity of each substance provided by your teacher. Record the conductivity in the data table. (NOTE: Dispose of each substance as instructed. Carefully rinse your equipment— including the sensor—with clean water before testing each new substance.)

   ◆ If the substance is a solid, mix a small spoonful of it with about 50 mL of fresh water. Test the resulting mixture.

   ◆ If the substance is a liquid, simply pour about 50 mL into the beaker. Test it as you did the mixtures of solids in water.

SHEDDING LIGHT ON CHEMICAL BONDS *(continued)*

◆ **Data Table**

Sample	Conductivity	Ionic or Covalent Bonds
Water		
Sodium chloride in water		

◆ **Analyze and Conclude**

Write your answers on the back of this sheet or on a separate sheet of paper.

1. Why did you test plain water first?

2. Based on your observations, indicate whether each substance tested contained ionic or covalent bonds.

3. Explain why one substance is a better conductor of electricity than another.

4. Did all the substances that conducted electricity show the same amount of conductivity? If not, what may have caused the differences?

5. **Think About It** How might varying the amount of each substance added to the water have affected your results? How could you better control the amount of each substance?

◆ **Design an Experiment**

Design another experiment to compare a different property of compounds containing ionic and covalent bonds. You might want to examine properties such as melting point, whether the substances dissolve in water, or whether the substances dissolve in some other liquid. Present your experimental plan to your teacher before proceeding.

PASCO

PASCO version

SKILLS LAB

You, the Consumer

PASCO

Sticky Sneakers

The appropriate sneaker for an activity should have a specific type of tread to grip the floor or the ground. In this lab you will test different sneakers by measuring the amount of friction between the sneakers and a table.

◆ **Problem** How does the amount of friction between a sneaker and a surface compare for different types of sneakers?

◆ **Skills Focus** forming operational definitions, measuring, controlling variables

◆ **Materials**

three or more different types of sneakers mass set(s)
USB Link   tape
PASPORT Force Sensor   3 large paper clips

◆ **Procedure** 🏃 *Review the safety guidelines in Appendix A.*

1. Sneakers are designed to deal with various friction forces, including these:
   ◆ Starting friction, which is involved when you start from a stopped position
   ◆ Forward-stopping friction, which is involved when you come to a forward stop
   ◆ Sideways-stopping friction, which is involved when you come to a sideways stop

2. Plug the USB Link into the computer's USB port.

3. Plug the force sensor into the USB Link.

This will automatically launch the PASPORTAL window.

I found a new PASPort sensor!
How would you like to use it?

Sticky Sneakers WB.ds

Workbook

EZ-Screen   DataStudio   Exit

STICKY SNEAKERS *(continued)*

4. Choose the appropriate electronic workbook *or* the proper DataStudio configuration file.

   ➤ If you are going to use the PASCO electronic workbook specifically designed for this activity, then simply click on the workbook entitled

   Sticky Sneakers WB.ds

   and go!

   ➤ If you are *not* using an electronic workbook, then click on the DataStudio icon and then from the menu bar, select File > Open Activity.   Next, choose

   Sticky Sneakers CF.ds

   and proceed with the following instructions.

5. Find the mass of each sneaker. Add masses inside each sneaker so that the *total* mass of the sneaker plus the masses is 1000 g. Spread the masses out evenly inside the sneaker.

6. Use the data table to record your data.

7. You will need to tape a paper clip to each sneaker and then attach the force sensor hook to the paper clip. To measure

   ◆ starting friction, attach the paper clip to the back of the sneaker.

   ◆ forward-stopping friction, attach the paper clip to the front of the sneaker.

   ◆ sideways-stopping friction, attach the paper clip to the side of the sneaker.

8. Press the ZERO button on the top of the force sensor to prepare the sensor before you start using it.

9. Click on the Start button ▶ Start .

10. To measure starting friction, pull the sneaker backward until it starts to move. Watch the graph.

11. Drag the sneaker backward for a few seconds and then click on the Stop button ■ Stop .

PASCO

STICKY SNEAKERS (*continued*)

12. The friction force is equal to the largest amount of force needed to make the sneaker start moving. In the graph, use the Smart Tool 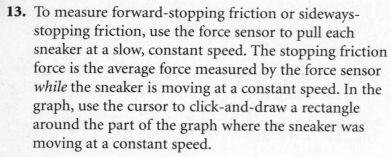 to find the starting friction force and record it in your data table. (*NOTE:* Click on the Smart Tool button in the graph tool bar. Move the Smart Tool to the point in the graph where the sneaker started moving. The second number next to the Smart Tool is the amount of force.)

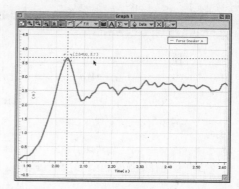

13. To measure forward-stopping friction or sideways-stopping friction, use the force sensor to pull each sneaker at a slow, constant speed. The stopping friction force is the average force measured by the force sensor *while* the sneaker is moving at a constant speed. In the graph, use the cursor to click-and-draw a rectangle around the part of the graph where the sneaker was moving at a constant speed.

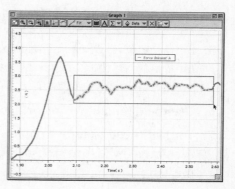

14. Click on the Statistics menu and select Mean. The average force measured by the sensor appears in the Legend Box in the graph. Record the stopping forces in your data table.

15. Repeat the steps of the procedure for the remaining sneakers.

◆ **Data Table**

Sneaker	Starting Friction (N)	Sideways-Stopping Friction (N)	Forward-Stopping Friction (N)
A			
B			
C			
D			
E			
F			

STICKY SNEAKERS *(continued)*

PASCO

◆ Analyze and Conclude

Answer the following questions on the back of this sheet or on a separate sheet of paper.

1. What are the manipulated and responding variables in this experiment? Explain.

2. Why is the reading on the force sensor equal to the friction force in each case?

3. Do you think that using a sneaker with a small amount of mass in it is a fair test of the friction of the sneakers? (Consider the fact that sneakers are used with people's feet inside them.) Explain your answer.

4. Draw a diagram that shows the forces acting on the sneaker for each type of motion.

5. Why did you pull the sneaker at a slow speed to test for stopping friction? For starting friction, why did you pull a sneaker that wasn't moving?

6. Which sneaker had the most starting friction? Which had the most forward-stopping friction? Which had the most sideways-stopping friction?

7. Can you identify a relationship between the type of sneaker and the type of friction you observed? What do you observe about the sneakers that would cause one to have better traction than another?

8. **Apply** Wear a pair of your own sneakers. Start running and notice how you press against the floor with your sneaker. How do you think this affects the friction between the sneaker and the floor? How can you test for this variable?

◆ Getting Involved

Go to a store that sells sneakers. If possible take a spring scale and, with the clerk's permission, do a quick friction test on sneakers designed for different activities. Also, note the materials they are made of, the support they provide for your feet, and other features. Then decide whether it is necessary to buy specific sneakers for different activities.

Controlling Variables

Sunny Rays and Angles

In this lab, you will investigate how the angle of the sun's rays affects the amount of energy absorbed by different parts of Earth's surface.

◆ **Problem**   How does the angle of a light source affect the rate of temperature change of a surface?

◆ **Materials**

3 USB Links	ruler
3 PASPORT Temperature Sensors	protractor
USB Hub	clear tape
books	100-W incandescent lamp
pencil	black construction paper
scissors	

◆ **Procedure**   🧤 ✂️   *Review the safety guidelines in Appendix A.*

1. Plug the USB Hub into the computer's USB port.
2. Plug one of the USB Links into the first port on the USB hub.
3. Plug one of the temperature sensors into the first USB Link.

This will automatically launch the PASPORTAL window.

I found a new PASPort sensor!
How would you like to use it?

Sunny Rays and Angles WB.ds

Workbook

EZ-Screen   DataStudio   Exit

© Prentice-Hall, Inc.

SUNNY RAYS AND ANGLES *(continued)*

4. Choose the appropriate electronic workbook *or* the proper DataStudio configuration file.

   ➤ If you are going to use the PASCO electronic workbook specifically designed for this activity, then simply click on the workbook entitled

   Sunny Rays and Angles WB.ds

   and go!

   ➤ If you are *not* using an electronic workbook, then click on the DataStudio icon and then from the menu bar, select File > Open Activity.   Next, choose

   Sunny Rays and Angles CF.ds

   and proceed with the following instructions.

5. Plug the second and third temperature sensors into the other two USB Links. Plug these links into the USB hub.

6. Cut a strip of black construction paper 5 cm by 10 cm. Fold the paper in half and tape two sides to form a pocket.

7. Repeat Step 6 to make two more pockets.

8. Place one pocket on the tip of each temperature sensor.

9. Place the pockets with temperature sensors close together, as shown in the diagram. Place the first temperature sensor you plugged into a USB Link in a vertical position (90° angle). Place the second temperature sensor at a 45° angle. Place the third temperature sensor in a horizontal position (0° angle). *NOTE:* The third temperature sensor should be positioned so that it is flat on the table. Use a protractor to measure the angles. Support the temperature sensors with books. Ensure that the paper pockets stay properly aligned with each sensor.

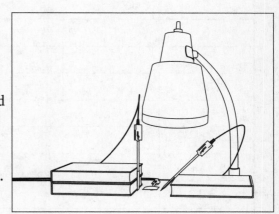

10. Position the lamp so that it is directly above and approximately 30 cm from each of the pockets. Make sure the lamp will not move during the activity.

11. Use the data table to record your data.

12. Click on the Start button ► Start .

13. In your data table, record the temperature measurement from each of the three temperature sensors in the Start row. (All three temperatures should be about the same.)

PASCO

SUNNY RAYS AND ANGLES *(continued)*

14. Switch on the lamp. In your data table, record the temperature measurement of each temperature sensor every minute for 15 minutes. **CAUTION:** *Be careful not to touch the hot lampshade.*

15. After 15 minutes, switch off the lamp.

16. Click on the Stop button [■ Stop] .

◆ Data Table

Time (min.)	Temperature (°C)		
	0° Angle	45° Angle	90° Angle
Start			
1			
2			
3			
4			
5			
6			
7			
8			
9			
10			
11			
12			
13			
14			
15			

SUNNY RAYS AND ANGLES *(continued)*

◆ Analyze and Conclude

Write your answers on the back of this sheet or on a separate sheet of paper.

1. In this experiment, what was the manipulated variable? What was the responding variable? How do you know which is which?

2. Examine your graph of temperature versus time. Based on your data, at which angle did the temperature increase the most?

3. At which angle did the temperature increase the least?

4. What part of Earth's surface does each temperature sensor represent?

5. Why is air at the North Pole still very cold in the summer even though the Northern Hemisphere is tilted toward the sun?

6. **Think About It** In this experiment, what variables were held constant?

◆ Design an Experiment

Design an experiment to find out how the results of this investigation would change if the lamp were placed farther away from the temperature sensors. Then design another experiment to find out what would happen if the lamp were placed closer to the temperature sensors.

Texas Instruments version   **REAL-WORLD LAB**

You and Your Community

Angling for Access

You and your friends have volunteered to help build a wheelchair-access ramp for the local public library. The design of the ramp has not been decided upon yet, so you need to build a model inclined plane. The model will help you determine what the steepness of the ramp should be.

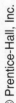

◆ **Problem**   How does the steepness of a wheelchair-access ramp affect its usefulness?

◆ **Skills Focus**   making models, measuring, calculating

◆ **Materials**

board, at least 10 cm wide and 50 cm long   metric ruler
wooden block with eye-hook   4 books, about 2 cm thick
Vernier Dual-Range Force Sensor   marker
DataMate calculator program   paper clip

◆ **Procedure**

1. Preview the following steps that describe how you can construct and use a ramp. Use the data table to record your data.

2. Prepare the force sensor for data collection.
   a. Connect the force sensor to Channel 1 of the LabPro or CBL 2 unit.
   b. If you are using a Dual-Range Force Sensor, there is a force range switch on the probe body; set the switch to the lowest setting.
   c. Use the link cable to connect the TI Graphing Calculator to the interface. Firmly press in the cable ends.

3. Turn on the calculator and start the DATAMATE program. Press CLEAR to reset the program.

4. Set up the calculator and interface for the correct force sensor.
   a. If the calculator displays the correct force sensor in CH 1, proceed directly to Step 7. If it does not, continue with this step to set up your sensor manually.
   b. Select SETUP from the main screen.
   c. Press ENTER to select CH1.
   d. Choose FORCE from the SELECT SENSOR list.
   e. Choose one of DUAL R FORCE (5N), DUAL R FORCE (10N), or STUDENT FORCE as appropriate for your force sensor from the FORCE list.
   f. Select OK to return to the main screen.

Angling for Access *(continued)*

5. The output force with an inclined plane is equal to the weight of the object. Lift the block with the force sensor to measure its weight. Record this value in the data table.

6. Make a mark on the side of the board about 3 cm from one end. Measure the length from the other end of the board to the mark, and record it in the data table.

7. Place one end of the board on top of a book. The mark you made on the board should be even with the edge of the book.

8. Measure the vertical distance in centimeters from the top of the table to where the underside of the incline touches the book. Record this value in the data table as "Height of Incline."

9. Get a wooden block with a hook on one end. Partly straighten a paper clip—leaving a hook at each end. Use the paper clip to attach the wooden block to your force sensor.

10. Lay the wooden block on its largest side. To measure the input force, slowly pull the wooden block up the inclined plane. The force sensor should be held parallel to, and about 2 cm above, the surface of the inclined plane, as shown in Figure 1. Once the wooden block is moving at a steady rate, select START to begin data collection. Continue pulling the wooden block until data collection is complete (3.0 seconds).

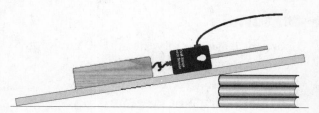

11. Determine the mean (average) force (in N) to pull the block up the inclined plane.

    a. Press ENTER to return to the main screen.

    b. Select ANALYZE from main screen.

    c. Select STATISTICS from the ANALYZE OPTIONS.

    d. Press ENTER to select the left boundary.

    e. Now select the other edge. Move the cursor to the right edge of the graph. Press ENTER, and wait while the calculator selects the data.

    f. Read the mean force from the calculator and record the value as the input force in your data table.

    g. Press ENTER, and select RETURN TO MAIN SCREEN.

© Prentice-Hall, Inc.

Angling for Access *(continued)*

12. Predict how your results will change if you repeat the investigation using two, three, and four books. Test your predictions. Make sure to zero the sensor whenever the angle of the inclined plane is changed.

13. For each trial, calculate the ideal mechanical advantage and the actual mechanical advantage. Record the calculations in your data table.

◆ Data Table

Number of Books	Output Force (N)	Length of Incline (cm)	Height of Incline (cm)	Input Force (N)	Ideal Mechanical Advantage	Actual Mechanical Advantage
1						
2						
3						
4						

◆ Analyze and Conclude

Write your answers on the back of this sheet or on a separate sheet of paper.

1. How did the ideal mechanical advantage and the actual mechanical advantage compare each time you repeated the experiment? Explain your answer.

2. Why do you write ideal and actual mechanical advantage without units?

3. What happens to the mechanical advantage as the inclined plane gets steeper? On the basis of this fact alone, which of the four inclined planes models the best steepness for a wheelchair-access ramp?

4. What other factors, besides mechanical advantage, should you consider when deciding on the steepness of the ramp?

5. **Apply** Suppose the door of the local public library is 2 m above the ground and the distance from the door to the parking lot is 15 m. How would these conditions affect your decision about how steep to make the ramp?

◆ Getting Involved

Find actual ramps that provide access for people with disabilities. Measure the heights and lengths of these ramps and calculate their ideal mechanical advantages. Find out what the requirements are for access ramps in your area. Should your ramp be made of a particular material? Should it level off before it reaches the door? How wide should it be? How does it provide water drainage?

Texas Instruments

Heart Beat, Health Beat

◆ **Problem** How does physical activity affect your pulse rate?

◆ **Materials**

Vernier Exercise Heart Rate Monitor
DataMate calculator program

◆ **Procedure** *Review the safety guidelines in Appendix A.*

1. Predict how your heart rate will change as you go from resting to being active, then back to resting again. Then copy the data table into your notebook.

2. Plug the exercise heart rate monitor into Channel 1 of the LabPro or CBL 2 interface. Use the link cable to connect the TI Graphing Calculator to the interface. Firmly press in the cable ends.

3. Turn on the calculator and start the DATAMATE program. Press CLEAR to reset the program.

4. Set up the calculator and interface for the exercise heart rate monitor.
   a. Select SETUP from the main screen.
   b. If the calculator displays EX HEART RT (BPM) in CH 1, proceed directly to Step 5. If it does not, continue with this step to set up your sensor manually.
   c. Press ENTER to select CH 1.
   d. Select HEART RATE from the SELECT SENSOR menu.
   e. Select EX HEART RT (BPM) from the HEART RATE menu.

5. Set up the calculator and interface for data collection.
   a. Use ▲ and ▼ to select MODE and press ENTER .
   b. Select TIME GRAPH from the SELECT MODE menu.
   c. Select CHANGE TIME SETTINGS from the TIME GRAPH SETTINGS menu.
   d. Enter 5 as the time between samples in seconds.
   e. Enter 84 as the number of samples. Data collection will last 420 seconds.
   f. Select OK to return to the setup screen.
   g. Select OK again to return to the main screen.

6. Depending upon your size, select a small or large size elastic strap. Secure one of the plastic ends of the elastic strap to the transmitter belt. It is important that the strap provide a snug fit of the transmitter belt.

Heart Beat, Health Beat *(continued)*

7. Wet each of the electrodes (the two grooved rectangular areas on the underside of the transmitter belt) with 3 drops of saline solution.

8. Secure the transmitter belt against the skin directly over the base of the rib cage. The POLAR logo on the front of the belt should be centered. Adjust the elastic strap to ensure a tight fit.

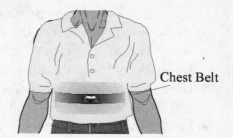

Chest Belt

9. Take the receiver module of the heart rate monitor in your right hand and stand quietly. Remember that the receiver must be within 80 cm of the transmitter in the heart rate monitor belt.

10. Once the subject has been standing quietly for about a minute, a partner should select START to begin monitoring heart rate. Stand quietly for 60 seconds. **CAUTION:** *Do not complete the rest of these procedures if there is any medical reason why you should avoid physical activities.*

11. When 60 seconds have gone by, begin to walk in place. It is necessary to walk in place for 60 seconds.

12. After 60 seconds of walking, begin running in place. Continue to run in place for 60 seconds.

13. After 60 seconds of running in place, stop running. Sit down right away and remain so until data collection stops. Data collection will end after you have rested for a total of 4 minutes.

14. Determine the resting heart rate.
    a. Press ENTER to return to the main screen.
    b. Select ANALYZE from the main screen.
    c. Select STATISTICS from the ANALYZE OPTIONS menu.
    d. Press ENTER to select the left bound of your region.
    e. Use ▶ to move the cursor to the point where the *x* value is equal to 60. Press ENTER to select the right bound of your region.
    f. Record the MEAN (average) heart rate (to the nearest whole bpm). This is the subject's standing heart rate.

15. Determine the heart rate after walking.
    a. Press ENTER to return to the ANALYZE OPTIONS menu.
    b. Select RETURN TO MAIN SCREEN from the ANALYZE OPTIONS menu.
    c. Select GRAPH from the main menu.
    d. Use ▶ to move the cursor to the highest point between 60 and 120 seconds on the graph.
    e. Record the heart rate (to the nearest whole bpm) displayed for this point.

Texas Instruments

Name _____ Date _____ Class _____

Heart Beat, Health Beat *(continued)*

16. Determine the heart rate after running.
    a. Press ENTER to return to the ANALYZE OPTIONS menu.
    b. Select RETURN TO MAIN SCREEN from the ANALYZE OPTIONS menu.
    c. Select GRAPH from the main menu.
    d. Use ▶ to move the cursor to the highest point between 120 and 180 seconds on the graph.
    e. Record the heart rate (to the nearest whole bpm) displayed for this point.

17. Determine the heart rate after resting for 1 minute.
    a. Move the cursor to the point at 240 seconds on the graph.
    b. Record the heart rate (HRT) displayed for this point.

18. Determine the heart rate after resting for 3 minutes.
    a. Move the cursor to the last point on the graph.
    b. Record the heart rate (HRT) displayed for this point.

19. Sketch or print the graph as directed by your teacher.

◆ **Data Table**

Activity	Pulse Rate
Resting	
Walking	
Running	
Resting after Exercise	
(1 min) Resting after Exercise	
(3+ min) Resting after Exercise	

Texas Instruments

© Prentice-Hall, Inc.

Heart Beat, Health Beat *(continued)*

◆ Analyze and Conclude

Write your answers on the back of this sheet or on a separate sheet of paper.

1. Use the data you obtained to create a bar graph of your pulse rate under the different conditions you tested.

2. What conclusion can you draw about the relationship between physical activity and a person's pulse rate?

3. What happens to the pulse rate when the physical activity has stopped?

4. What can you infer about the heartbeat when the pulse rate increases?

5. **Think About It** Do you think the pulse measurements you made are completely accurate? Why or why not? How could you improve the accuracy of your measurements?

◆ Design an Experiment

Do the resting pulse rates of adults, teens, and young children differ? Write a plan to answer this question. Obtain your teacher's permission before carrying out your plan.

Texas Instruments

Developing Hypotheses

Heating Earth's Surface

In this lab, you will develop and test a hypothesis about how quickly different materials absorb radiation.

◆ **Problem** How do the heating and cooling rates of sand and water compare?

◆ **Materials**

2 Vernier Temperature Probes
DataMate calculator program
ring stand and 2 ring clamps
sand, 300 mL
water, 300 mL
string

2 beakers, 400 mL
metric ruler
lamp with 150-W bulb
clock or stopwatch
graph paper

◆ **Procedure**   *Review the safety guidelines in Appendix A.*

1. Do you think that sand or water will heat up faster? Record your hypothesis on a separate sheet of paper. Explain what information you used to form your hypothesis. Then follow the steps below to test your hypothesis.

2. Plug Temperature Probe 1 into Channel 1 of the LabPro or CBL 2 interface. Plug Temperature Probe 2 into Channel 2. Use the link cable to connect the TI Graphing Calculator to the interface. Firmly press in the cable ends.

3. Turn on the calculator and start the DATAMATE program. Press CLEAR to reset the program.

4. Set up the calculator and interface for the two temperature probes.
   a. Select SETUP from the main screen.
   b. If the calculator displays the correct temperature probes in CH 1 and CH 2, proceed directly to Step 5. If it does not, continue with this step to set up your sensors manually.
   c. Press ENTER to select CH 1.
   d. Select TEMPERATURE from the SELECT SENSOR menu.
   e. Select the correct temperature probe (in °C) from the TEMPERATURE menu.
   f. Use ▼ to select CH 2, then press ENTER .
   g. Select TEMPERATURE from the SELECT SENSOR menu.
   h. Select the correct temperature probe (in °C) from the TEMPERATURE menu.

Texas Instruments

Heating Earth's Surface *(continued)*

5. Set up the calculator and interface for data collection.
  a. Use ⬆ and ⬇ to select MODE and press ⏎ .
  b. Select TIME GRAPH from the SELECT MODE menu.
  c. Select CHANGE TIME SETTINGS from the TIME GRAPH SETTINGS menu.
  d. Enter 30 as the time between samples in seconds.
  e. Enter 30 as the number of samples. Data collection will last 900 seconds (15 minutes).
  f. Select OK to return to the setup screen.
  g. Select OK again to return to the main screen.

6. Fill one beaker with 300 mL of dry sand.

7. Fill the second beaker with 300 mL of water at room temperature.

8. Arrange the beakers beneath the ring stand.

9. Place one temperature probe in each beaker.

10. Suspend the temperature probes from the ring stand with string. This will hold the probes in place so they do not fall.

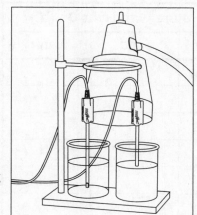

11. Adjust the height of the clamp so that the tip of each probe is covered by about 0.5 cm of sand or water in a beaker.

12. Position the lamp so that it is about 20 cm above the sand and water. There should be no more than 8 cm between the beakers. **CAUTION:** *Be careful not to splash water onto the hot light bulb.*

13. Select START to begin data collection. After you hear a beep, switch on the light bulb. Data collection will end automatically after 15 minutes.

14. Record your beginning and final temperatures.
  a. When data collection is complete after 15 minutes, a graph of temperature vs. time will be displayed. Use ➡ to examine data points along the curve for Probe 1. As you move the cursor right or left, the time (X) and temperature (Y) values of each data point are displayed below the graph. *NOTE:* P1 appears in the upper right corner of the screen.
  b. Record the beginning and final temperatures for Probe 1 (to the nearest 0.1°C).
  c. Use ⬆ to move the cursor to the curve for Probe 2. *NOTE:* P2 now appears in the upper right corner of the screen. Use ➡ to examine data points along the curve for Probe 2.
  d. Record the beginning and final temperatures for Probe 2 (to the nearest 0.1°C).
  e. Press ⏎ to return to the main screen.

Texas Instruments

Heating Earth's Surface *(continued)*

15. Which material do you think will cool off more quickly? Record your hypothesis on a separate sheet of paper. Again, give reasons why you think your hypothesis is correct.

16. Turn the light off. Repeat Steps 13–14 to test your hypothesis for cooling.

◆ Data Table

Temperature with Light On (°C)			Temperature with Light Off (°C)		
Time (min)	Sand	Water	Time (min)	Sand	Water
Start			16		
1			17		
2			18		
3			19		
4			20		
5			21		
6			22		
7			23		
8			24		
9			25		
10			26		
11			27		
12			28		
13			29		
14			30		
15					

Texas Instruments

© Prentice-Hall, Inc.

Heating Earth's Surface *(continued)*

◆ Analyze and Conclude

Write your answers on a separate sheet of paper.

1. Calculate the total change in temperature for each material.

2. Based on your data, which material had the greater increase in temperature?

3. What can you conclude about which material absorbed heat faster? How do your results compare with your hypothesis?

4. Review your data again. In 15 minutes, which material cooled faster?

5. How do these results compare to your second hypothesis?

6. **Think About It** If your results did not support either of your hypotheses, why do you think the results differed from what you expected?

7. **Apply** Based on your results, which do you think will heat up more quickly on a sunny day: the water in a lake or the sand surrounding it? Which will cool off more quickly after dark?

◆ More to Explore

Do you think all solid materials heat up as fast as sand? For example, consider gravel, crushed stone, or different types of soil. Write a hypothesis about their heating rates. With the approval and supervision of your teacher, develop a procedure to test your hypothesis. Was your hypothesis correct?

Texas Instruments

Just Add Water

If you add hot water to cold water, what will happen? In this lab, you'll make a device that measures changes in thermal energy. It is called a calorimeter. You will use the skill of interpreting data to calculate the thermal energy transferred.

◆ **Problem** When hot and cold water are mixed, how much thermal energy is transferred from the hot water to the cold water?

◆ **Materials**

Vernier Temperature Probe   balance
DataMate calculator program   pencil
4 plastic foam cups   beaker of water kept in an ice bath
hot tap water   scissors

Making a Calorimeter

A. Label a plastic foam cup with the letter C ("C" stands for cold water).
B. Cut 2 to 3 cm from the top of a second plastic foam cup. Invert the second cup over the first. Label the cover with a C also. The cup and cover are your cold water calorimeter.
C. Using a pencil, poke a hole in the cover large enough for a temperature probe to fit snugly.
D. Repeat Steps A, B, and C with two other plastic foam cups. This time label both cup and cover with an H. This is your hot water calorimeter.

◆ **Procedure** *Review the safety guidelines in Appendix A.*

1. Predict how the amount of thermal energy lost by hot water will be related to the amount of thermal energy gained by cold water.

2. Record all data in the data table.

3. Follow the instructions in the box to make two calorimeters. Find the mass of each empty calorimeter (including the cover) on a balance and record each mass in your data table.

4. Plug the temperature probe into Channel 1 of the LabPro or CBL 2 interface. Use the link cable to connect the TI Graphing Calculator to the interface. Firmly press in the cable ends.

JUST ADD WATER (continued)

5. Turn on the calculator and start the DATAMATE program. Press CLEAR to reset the program.

6. Set up the calculator and interface for the temperature probe.
   a. Select SETUP from the main screen.
   b. If the calculator displays the correct temperature probe in CH 1, proceed directly to Step 7. If it does not, continue with this step to set up your sensor manually.
   c. Press ENTER to select CH 1.
   d. Select TEMPERATURE from the SELECT SENSOR menu.
   e. Select the correct temperature probe (in °C) from the TEMPERATURE menu.

7. Set up the calculator and interface for data collection.
   a. Use ▲ and ▼ to select MODE and press ENTER .
   b. Select SINGLE POINT from the SELECT MODE menu.
   c. Select OK to return to the main screen.

8. From a beaker of water that has been sitting in an ice bath, add water (no ice cubes) to the cold-water calorimeter. Fill it about one third full. Put the cover on, find the total mass, and record the mass in your data table.

9. Add hot tap water to the hot-water calorimeter. Fill it about one third full. **CAUTION:** *Hot tap water can cause burns.* Put the cover on, find the total mass, and record the mass in your data table.

10. Calculate the mass of the water in each calorimeter. Record the results in your data table.

11. Put the temperature probe through the hole in the cover of the cold-water calorimeter. Wait 30 seconds and then select START to find the temperature. Record the temperature of the calorimeter in your data table. Press ENTER to return to the main screen.

12. Repeat Step 11 for the hot-water calorimeter.

13. Remove the temperature probe and both covers. Pour the water from the cold-water calorimeter into the hot-water calorimeter. Put the cover back on the hot-water calorimeter, and repeat Step 11 to find the temperature. Record the temperature as the final temperature for both calorimeters.

Texas Instruments

JUST ADD WATER *(continued)*

◆ Data Table

	Mass of Empty Cup (g)	Mass of Cup and Water (g)	Mass of Water (g)	Starting Temp. (°C)	Final Temp. (°C)	Change in Temp. (°C)
Cold Water Calorimeter						
Hot Water Calorimeter						

◆ Analyze and Conclude

Write your answers on the back of this sheet or on a separate sheet of paper.

1. What is the temperature change of the cold water? Record your answer in the data table.

2. What is the temperature change of the hot water? Record your answer in the data table.

3. Calculate the amount of thermal energy that enters the cold water by using the formula for the transfer of thermal energy. The specific heat of water is 4.18 J/(g•K), so you use the following formula.

    Thermal energy transferred = 4.18 J/(g•K) × Mass of cold water × Temperature change of cold water. Remember that 1°C is equal to 1 K.

4. Now use the formula to calculate the thermal energy leaving the hot water.

5. What unit should you use for your results for Questions 3 and 4?

6. Was your prediction from Step 1 confirmed? How do you know?

7. **Think About It** What sources of error might have affected your results? How could the lab be redesigned in order to reduce the errors?

◆ Design an Experiment

How would your results be affected if you started with much more hot water than cold? If you used more cold water than hot? Make a prediction. Then design a procedure to test your prediction. Get your teacher's approval, and try your new procedure.

Texas Instruments

Texas Instruments version

Designing Experiments

Keeping Comfortable

Two ways to use less energy are to keep heat out of your home when the weather is hot, and to keep heat in when the weather is cold. In this lab, you will design an experiment to compare how well different materials do this.

◆ **Problem** How well do different materials stop heat transfer?

◆ **Materials**

> Vernier Temperature Probe
> DataMate calculator program
> hot water
> ice water
> beakers
> containers and lids made of paper, plastic foam, plastic, glass, and metal

◆ **Design a Plan**   *Review the safety guidelines in Appendix A.*

◆ **Part 1 Measuring Temperature Changes**

1. Plug the temperature probe into Channel 1 of the LabPro or CBL 2 interface. Use the link cable to connect the TI Graphing Calculator to the interface. Firmly press in the cable ends.

2. Turn on the calculator and start the DATAMATE program. Press ⌈CLEAR⌉ to reset the program.

3. Set up the calculator and interface for the temperature probe.
   a. Select SETUP from the main screen.
   b. If the calculator displays the correct temperature probe in CH 1, proceed directly to Step 4. If it does not, continue with this step to set up your sensor manually.
   c. Press ⌈ENTER⌉ to select CH 1.
   d. Select TEMPERATURE from the SELECT SENSOR menu.
   e. Select the correct temperature probe (in °C) from the TEMPERATURE menu.

4. Set up the calculator and interface for data collection.
   a. Use ⌈▲⌋ and ⌈▼⌋ to select MODE and press ⌈ENTER⌉ .
   b. Select TIME GRAPH from the SELECT MODE menu.
   c. Select CHANGE TIME SETTINGS from the TIME GRAPH SETTINGS menu.
   d. Enter 10 as the time between samples in seconds.
   e. Enter 60 as the number of samples. Data collection will last 600 seconds (10 minutes).
   f. Select OK to return to the setup screen.
   g. Select OK again to return to the main screen.

KEEPING COMFORTABLE (continued)

5. Use a pencil to poke a hole in the lid of a paper cup. Fill the cup about halfway with cold water.

6. Put the lid on the cup. Insert a temperature probe into the water through the hole. When the temperature stops dropping, place the cup in a beaker. Add hot water to the beaker until the water level is about 1 cm below the lid.

7. Select START to begin collecting data. Continue collecting data until the temperature has increased by 5°C. Press ■Stop to stop data collection. Use the time it takes for the temperature to increase 1°C as a measure of the effectiveness of the paper cup.

◆ Part 2 Comparing Materials

8. Use the ideas from Part 1 to design a controlled experiment to rank the effectiveness of different materials in preventing heat transfer.

9. Use the following questions to help you plan your experiment. Write your plan on the next page.
   ◆ What hypothesis will you test?
   ◆ Which materials do you predict will be the best and worst at preventing heat transfer?
   ◆ What will your manipulated variable be? What will your responding variable be?
   ◆ What variables do you need to control? How will you control them?
   ◆ What step-by-step procedures will you use?
   ◆ What kind of data table will you use?

10. After your teacher has reviewed your plans, make any necessary changes in your design. Then perform your experiment.

◆ Analyze and Conclude

1. In Part 1, what was the starting temperature of the hot water? What was the starting temperature of the cold water? In which direction did the heat flow? How do you know?

2. If the materials in Part 1 are used to represent your home in very hot weather, which material would represent the rooms in your home? Which would represent the outdoor weather? Which would represent the walls of the building?

3. Which material was most effective at blocking the transfer of heat? Which was the least effective? Explain.

4. **Think About It** Would experiments similar to this one provide you with enough information to choose materials to build a home? Explain.

Texas Instruments

KEEPING COMFORTABLE *(continued)*

◆ More to Explore

Create a plan to compare how well the materials would work if the hot water were inside the cup and the cold water were outside. With your teacher's permission, carry out your plan.

EXPERIMENT PLAN

Write your experiment plan below. If you need more room, use a separate sheet of paper.

◆ Hypothesis

_____

_____

◆ Materials

_____

_____

_____

◆ Procedure

_____

_____

_____

_____

_____

◆ Data Table

© Prentice-Hall, Inc.

Texas Instruments

Texas Instruments

Melting Ice

In this experiment, you will measure temperature as you explore the melting of ice.

◆ **Problem**   How does the temperature of the surroundings affect the rate at which ice melts?

◆ **Materials**

Vernier Temperature Probe
DataMate calculator program
plastic cup, about 200 mL
ice cubes, about 2 cm on each side

warm water, about 40°C to 45°C
water at room temperature, about 20°C
stopwatch or timer

◆ **Procedure**   *Review the safety guidelines in Appendix A.*

1. Read Steps 1–14. Based on your own experience, predict which ice cube will melt faster.

2. In your notebook, make a data table like the one on the next page.

3. Plug the temperature probe into Channel 1 of the LabPro or CBL 2 interface. Use the link cable to connect the TI Graphing Calculator to the interface. Firmly press in the cable ends.

4. Turn on the calculator and start the DATAMATE program. Press CLEAR to reset the program.

5. Set up the calculator and interface for the temperature probe.
   a. Select SETUP from the main screen.
   b. If the calculator displays the correct temperature probe in CH 1, proceed directly to Step 6. If it does not, continue with this step to set up your sensor manually.
   c. Press ENTER to select CH 1.
   d. Select TEMPERATURE from the SELECT SENSOR menu.
   e. Select the correct temperature probe (in °C) from the TEMPERATURE menu.

6. Set up the calculator and interface for data collection.
   a. Use ▲ and ▼ to select MODE and press ENTER .
   b. Select TIME GRAPH from the SELECT MODE menu.
   c. Select CHANGE TIME SETTINGS from the TIME GRAPH SETTINGS menu.
   d. Enter 5 as the time between samples in seconds.
   e. Enter 60 as the number of samples. Data collection will last 300 seconds (5 minutes).
   f. Select OK to return to the setup screen.
   g. Select OK again to return to the main screen.

© Prentice-Hall, Inc.

MELTING ICE *(continued)*

7. Fill a cup halfway with warm water (about 40°C to 45°C).

8. Record the exact temperature of the water in the cup.

9. Obtain an ice cube that is roughly the same size as the other available ice cubes. Place the ice cube in the cup of water and select START to begin data collection. Begin timing with a stopwatch.

10. Using the temperature probe, gently stir the water in the cup until the ice cube in the cup has completely melted. Record the time at which the ice cube was completely melted. Do not stop data collection early; it will automatically stop after 5 minutes.

11. When data collection has finished, use ⬛▶ to move the cursor to the point on the graph where the ice cube was completely melted. Record the water temperature at that point in your data table. Press ENTER to return to the main screen.

12. Store the data from the first run so that it can be used later.
    a. Select TOOLS from the main screen.
    b. Select STORE LATEST RUN from the TOOLS MENU.

13. Empty the water from the cup and fill it halfway with water at room temperature.

14. Repeat Steps 8–11 to collect data.

◆ **Data Table**

	Beginning Temperature (°C)	Time to Melt (s)	Final Temperature (°C)
Cup 1			
Cup 2			

Texas Instruments

© Prentice-Hall, Inc.

MELTING ICE *(continued)*

◆ Analyze and Conclude

Write your answers on the back of this sheet or on a separate sheet of paper.

1. Was your prediction in Step 1 supported by the results of the experiment? Explain why or why not.

2. In which cup did the water temperature change the most? Explain this result.

3. When the ice melted, its molecules gained enough energy to overcome the forces holding them together as solid ice. What is the source of that energy?

4. **Think About It** How well could you time the exact moment that each ice cube completely melted? How might errors in measurements affect your conclusions?

◆ Design an Experiment

When a lake freezes in winter, only the top turns to ice. Design an experiment to model the melting of a frozen lake during the spring. With your teacher's approval, carry out your experiment. Be prepared to share your results with the class.

Texas Instruments

Shedding Light on Chemical Bonds

Electricity is the flow of electric current. In this lab, you will interpret data about which compounds conduct electricity in order to determine the nature of their bonds.

◆ **Problem**   How can you use a conductivity tester to determine whether a compound contains ionic or covalent bonds?

◆ **Materials**

Vernier Conductivity Probe   graduated cylinder, 100 mL
DataMate calculator program   small plastic spoon
small beaker   table salt
distilled water   additional substances provided by your teacher

◆ **Procedure**   *Review the safety guidelines in Appendix A.*

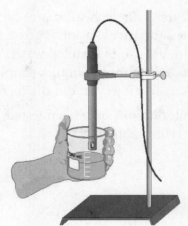

1. Use the data table to record your data.

2. Set up the conductivity probe with the ring stand and utility clamp as shown in Figure 1.

3. Plug the conductivity probe into Channel 1 of the LabPro or CBL 2 interface. Set the selector switch on the side of the conductivity probe to the 0–20,000 range. Use the link cable to connect the TI Graphing Calculator to the interface. Firmly press in the cable ends.

4. Turn on the calculator and start the DATAMATE program. Press CLEAR to reset the program.

5. Set up the calculator and interface for the Conductivity Probe.
   a. Select SETUP from the main screen.
   b. Press ENTER to select CH 1.
   c. Select CONDUCTIVITY from the SELECT SENSOR menu.
   d. Select CONDUCTIVITY 10000 (MG/L) from the CONDUCTIVITY menu.

SHEDDING LIGHT ON CHEMICAL BONDS *(continued)*

6. Set up the data-collection mode.

    a. To select MODE, press ☐▲☐ once and press ENTER .

    b. Select SINGLE POINT from the SELECT MODE menu.

    c. Select OK to return to the main screen.

7. Testing the conductivity of distilled water.

    a. Pour 200 mL of distilled water in a beaker and place the conductivity probe into it. The hole near the probe end must be completely submerged in the solution.

    b. Select START to begin collecting data. *Important:* Leave the probe tip submerged while data is being collected for the next 10 seconds.

    c. After 10 seconds, the conductivity value will appear on the calculator screen. Record this value in your data table.

    d. Press ENTER to return to the main screen.

    e. To avoid contaminating the solutions, rinse the probe with clean, distilled water after each test. Blot the outside of the probe dry with a tissue or paper towel. Do not worry about drying the inside of the hole near the tip of the probe.

8. Add a very small scoop of salt (1/8 teaspoon) to the beaker of distilled water. Stir the salt into the water until completely dissolved.

9. Repeat Step 7 using the salt water you just mixed.

10. Repeat Step 7 for each substance provided by your teacher.

    ◆ If the substance is a solid, mix a small spoonful (1/8 teaspoon) of it with about 200 mL of distilled water. Test the resulting mixture.

    ◆ If the substance is a liquid, simply pour about 100 mL into an empty beaker. Test it as you did the mixtures of solids in water.

11. When all solutions have been tested, select QUIT to exit the DATAMATE program.

Texas Instruments

SHEDDING LIGHT ON CHEMICAL BONDS *(continued)*

◆ Data Table

Sample	Conductivity	Ionic or Covalent Bonds
Water		
Sodium chloride in water		

◆ Analyze and Conclude

Write your answers on the back of this sheet or on a separate sheet of paper.

1. Why did you test plain water first?

2. Based on your observations, indicate whether each substance tested contained ionic or covalent bonds.

3. Explain why one substance is a better conductor of electricity than another.

4. Did all the substances that conducted electricity show the same amount of conductivity? If not, what might have caused the differences?

5. **Think About It** How might varying the amount of each substance added to the water have affected your results? How could you better control the amount of each substance?

◆ Design an Experiment

Design another experiment to compare a different property of compounds containing ionic and covalent bonds. You might want to examine properties such as melting point, whether the substances dissolve in water, or whether the substances dissolve in some other liquid. Present your experimental plan to your teacher before proceeding.

Texas Instruments

Texas Instruments version　　　**REAL-WORLD LAB**

You, the Consumer

Sticky Sneakers

The appropriate sneaker for an activity should have a specific type of tread to grip the floor or the ground. In this lab you will test different sneakers by measuring the amount of friction between the sneakers and a table.

◆ **Problem**　How does the amount of friction between a sneaker and a surface compare for different types of sneakers?

◆ **Skills Focus**　forming operational definitions, measuring, controlling variables

◆ **Materials**

three or more different types of sneakers
Vernier Dual-Range Force Sensor　　　　　large paper clip
DataMate calculator program　　　　　　　tape
mass set(s)　　　　　　　　　　　　　　　balance

◆ **Procedure** 🔃　*Review the safety guidelines in Appendix A.*

1. Sneakers are designed to deal with various friction forces, including these:
   ◆ starting friction, which is involved when you start from a stopped position
   ◆ forward-stopping friction, which is involved when you come to a forward stop
   ◆ sideways-stopping friction, which is involved when you come to a sideways stop

2. Use the data table to record your data.

3. Find the mass of each sneaker. Then put masses in each sneaker so that the total mass of the sneaker plus the masses is 1000 g. Spread the masses out evenly inside the sneaker.

4. Plug the force sensor into Channel 1 of the LabPro or CBL 2 interface. Use the link cable to connect the TI Graphing Calculator to the interface. Firmly press in the cable ends. If you are using a Dual-Range Force Sensor, set the range switch to 10 N.

5. Turn on the calculator and start the DATAMATE program. Press CLEAR to reset the program.

© Prentice-Hall, Inc.

STICKY SNEAKERS *(continued)*

6. Set up the calculator and interface for the force sensor.
  a. Select SETUP from the main screen.
  b. If the calculator displays a force sensor in CH 1, proceed directly to Step 4.
    If it does not, continue with this step to set up your sensor manually.
  c. Press ⌈ENTER⌉ to select CH 1.
  d. Select FORCE from the SELECT SENSOR menu.
  e. Select the correct force sensor and setting from the FORCE menu.

7. Set up the calculator and interface for data collection.
  a. Use ⌈▲⌉ and ⌈▼⌉ to select MODE and press ⌈ENTER⌉.
  b. Select TIME GRAPH from the SELECT MODE menu.
  c. Select CHANGE TIME SETTINGS from the TIME GRAPH SETTINGS menu.
  d. Enter 0.05 as the time between samples in seconds.
  e. Enter 100 as the number of samples. Data collection will last 5 seconds.
  f. Select OK to return to the setup screen.

8. Zero the force sensor.
  a. Lay the force sensor on the tabletop in the position shown below.

  b. Select ZERO from the SETUP menu.
  c. Select CH1-FORCE (N) from the SELECT CHANNEL menu.
  d. Press ⌈ENTER⌉ to zero the force sensor.

9. You will need to tape the paper clip to each sneaker and then attach a force sensor to the paper clip. To measure
  ◆ starting friction, attach the paper clip to the back of the sneaker.
  ◆ forward-stopping friction, attach the paper clip to the front of the sneaker.
  ◆ sideways-stopping friction, attach the paper clip to the side of the sneaker.

10. To measure starting friction, select START to begin data collection and slowly pull the sneaker backward with the force sensor until it starts to move.

Texas Instruments

STICKY SNEAKERS *(continued)*

11. The force necessary to make the sneaker start moving is equal to the friction force. Determine and record the starting friction value.
    a. After data collection stops, press [ENTER] to return to the main screen.
    b. Select ANALYZE from the main screen.
    c. Select STATISTICS from the ANALYZE OPTIONS menu.
    d. Press [ENTER] before moving the cursor.
    e. Use [►] to move the cursor to the right side of the screen and press [ENTER] .
    f. Record the MAX force (in N) as the starting friction force in your data table.
    g. Press [ENTER] , and select RETURN TO MAIN SCREEN.

12. To measure forward-stopping friction, attach the paper clip to the front of the sneaker and slowly pull it across the table at a constant speed. Once the sneaker is moving at a steady rate, select START to begin data collection.

13. Repeat Step 11 to determine the forward-stopping friction. Record the MEAN (average) force as the stopping force in your data table.

14. Attach the paper clip to the side of the sneaker and repeat Steps 12 and 13 to determine the last type of stopping friction.

15. Repeat Steps 9–14 for the remaining sneakers.

◆ Data Table

Sneaker	Starting Friction (N)	Sideways-Stopping Friction (N)	Forward-Stopping Friction (N)
A			
B			
C			
D			
E			
F			

Texas Instruments

© Prentice-Hall, Inc.

STICKY SNEAKERS *(continued)*

◆ Analyze and Conclude

Answer the following questions on the back of this sheet or on a separate sheet of paper.

1. What are the manipulated and responding variables in this experiment? Explain.

2. Why is the reading of the force sensor equal to the friction force in each case?

3. Do you think that using a sneaker with a small amount of mass in it is a fair test of the friction of the sneakers? (Consider the fact that sneakers are used with people's feet inside them.) Explain your answer.

4. Draw a diagram that shows the forces acting on the sneaker for each type of motion.

5. Why did you pull the sneaker at a slow speed to test for stopping friction? For starting friction, why did you pull a sneaker that wasn't moving?

6. Which sneaker had the most starting friction? Which had the most forward-stopping friction? Which had the most sideways-stopping friction?

7. Can you identify a relationship between the type of sneaker and the type of friction you observed? What do you observe about the sneakers that would cause one to have better traction than another?

8. **Apply** Wear a pair of your own sneakers. Start running and notice how you press against the floor with your sneaker. How do you think this affects the friction between the sneaker and the floor? How can you test for this variable?

◆ Getting Involved

Go to a store that sells sneakers. If possible take a spring scale and, with the clerk's permission, do a quick friction test on sneakers for different activities. Also, note the materials they are made of, the support they provide for your feet, and other features. Then decide whether it is necessary to buy specific sneakers for different activities.

Texas Instruments

Sunny Rays and Angles

In this lab, you will investigate how the angle of the sun's rays affects the amount of energy absorbed by different parts of Earth's surface.

◆ **Problem**   How does the angle of a light source affect the rate of temperature change of a surface?

◆ **Materials**

3 Vernier Temperature Probes   pencil
DataMate calculator program   metric ruler
books   100-W incandescent lamp
scissors   clear tape
black construction paper   protractor

◆ **Procedure**   *Review the safety guidelines in Appendix A.*

1. Cut a strip of black construction paper 5 cm by 10 cm. Fold the paper in half and tape two sides to form a pocket.

2. Repeat Step 1 to make two more pockets.

3. Place the tip of a temperature probe inside each pocket.

4. Place the pockets with temperature probes close together as shown in the figure below. Place one probe in a vertical position (90° angle), one at a 45° angle, and the third one in a horizontal position (0° angle). Use a protractor to measure the angles. Support the probes with books.

5. Position the lamp so that it is 30 cm from each of the probe tips. Make sure the lamp will not move during the activity.

6. Examine the data table on page 64.

7. Plug Temperature Probe 1 into Channel 1 of the LabPro or CBL 2 interface. Plug Temperature Probe 2 into Channel 2. Plug Temperature Probe 3 into Channel 3. Use the link cable to connect the TI Graphing Calculator to the interface. Firmly press in the cable ends.

8. Turn on the calculator and start the DATAMATE program. Press CLEAR to reset the program.

SUNNY RAYS AND ANGLES *(continued)*

9. Set up the calculator and interface for the three temperature probes.
   a. Select SETUP from the main screen.
   b. If the calculator displays the correct temperature probes in CH 1, CH 2, and CH 3, proceed directly to Step 10. If it does not, continue with this step to set up your sensors manually.
   c. Press ENTER to select CH 1.
   d. Select TEMPERATURE from the SELECT SENSOR menu.
   e. Select the correct temperature probe (in °C) from the TEMPERATURE menu.
   f. Use ▼ to select CH 2, then press ENTER .
   g. Select TEMPERATURE from the SELECT SENSOR menu.
   h. Select the correct temperature probe (in °C) from the TEMPERATURE menu.
   i. Use ▼ to select CH 3, then press ENTER .
   j. Select TEMPERATURE from the SELECT SENSOR menu.
   k. Select the correct temperature probe (in °C) from the TEMPERATURE menu.

10. Set up the calculator and interface for data collection.
    a. Use ▲ and ▼ to select MODE and press ENTER .
    b. Select TIME GRAPH from the SELECT MODE menu.
    c. Select CHANGE TIME SETTINGS from the TIME GRAPH SETTINGS menu.
    d. Enter 30 as the time between samples in seconds.
    e. Enter 30 as the number of samples. Data collection will last 900 seconds (15 minutes).
    f. Select OK to return to the setup screen.
    g. Select OK again to return to the main screen.

11. In the data table, record the current temperature of all three temperature probes. (All three temperatures should be the same.)

12. Switch on the lamp. Select START to begin data collection. In the data table, record the temperature of each probe every minute for 15 minutes.
    CAUTION: *Be careful not to touch the hot lampshade.*

13. Data collection will end automatically after 15 minutes. When this happens, switch off the lamp.

Texas Instruments

© Prentice-Hall, Inc.

SUNNY RAYS AND ANGLES *(continued)*

◆ **Data Table**

Time (min.)	Temperature (°C)		
	0° Angle	45° Angle	90° Angle
Start			
1			
2			
3			
4			
5			
6			
7			
8			
9			
10			
11			
12			
13			
14			
15			

Texas Instruments

© Prentice-Hall, Inc.

SUNNY RAYS AND ANGLES *(continued)*

◆ Analyze and Conclude

Write your answers on the back of this sheet or on a separate sheet of paper.

1. In this experiment, what was the manipulated variable? What was the responding variable? How do you know which is which?

2. Graph your data on a sheet of graph paper. Label the horizontal axis time (min.) and vertical axis temperature (°C). Use solid, dashed, and dotted lines to show the results from each temperature probe.

3. Based on your data, at which angle did the temperature increase the most?

4. At which angle did the temperature increase the least?

5. What part of Earth's surface does each temperature probe represent?

6. Why is air at the North Pole still very cold in the summer even though the Northern Hemisphere is tilted toward the sun?

7. **Think About It** In this experiment, what variables were held constant?

◆ Design an Experiment

Design an experiment to find out how the results of this investigation would change if the lamp were placed farther away from the temperature probes. Then design another experiment to find out what would happen if the lamp were placed closer to the temperature probes.

Texas Instruments

Vernier version   **REAL-WORLD LAB**

You and Your Community

Angling for Access

You and your friends have volunteered to help build a wheelchair-access ramp for the local public library. The design of the ramp has not been decided upon yet, so you need to build a model inclined plane. The model will help you determine what the steepness of the ramp should be.

◆ **Problem**   How does the steepness of a wheelchair-access ramp affect its usefulness?

◆ **Skills Focus**   making models, measuring, calculating

◆ **Materials**

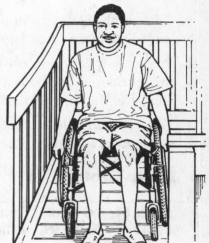

board, at least 10 cm wide and 50 cm long	metric ruler
	4 books, about 2 cm thick
wooden block with eye-hook	marker
Vernier Dual-Range Force Sensor	paper clip
Logger *Pro* computer software	

◆ **Procedure**

1. Preview the following steps that describe how you can construct and use a ramp. Use the data table to record your data.

2. Start the Logger *Pro* computer software. Prepare for data collection by opening the experiment file "Angling for Access." Be sure to open the file that matches the probe you are using.

3. The output force of an inclined plane is equal to the weight of the object. Lift the block with the force sensor to measure its weight. Record this value in the data table.

4. Make a mark on the side of the board about 3 cm from one end. Measure the length from the other end of the board to the mark and record it in the data table.

5. Place the marked end of the board on top of a book. The mark you made on the board should be even with the edge of the book.

6. Measure the vertical distance in centimeters from the top of the table to where the underside of the incline touches the book. Record this value in the data table as "Height of Incline."

Vernier

Angling for Access *(continued)*

7. Get a wooden block with an eyehook on one end. Partly straighten a paper clip, leaving a hook at each end. Use the paper clip to attach the wooden block to your force sensor.

8. Lay the wooden block on its largest side. To measure the input force, start pulling the block straight up the incline with the force sensor at a slow steady speed. Once the block is moving at a steady rate, click ▶Start to begin data collection. Be sure to hold the sensor parallel to the incline, as shown.

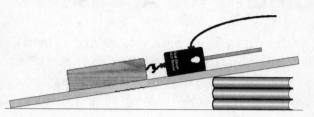

9. Click on the Statistics button, [STAT], and record the mean force (input force) in your data table.

10. Predict how your results will change if you repeat the investigation using two, three, and four books. Test your predictions. Make sure to zero the sensor whenever the angle of the inclined plane is changed.

11. For each trial, calculate the ideal mechanical advantage and the actual mechanical advantage. Record the calculations in your data table.

◆ Data Table

Number of Books	Output Force (N)	Length of Incline (cm)	Height of Incline (cm)	Input Force (N)	Ideal Mechanical Advantage	Actual Mechanical Advantage
1						
2						
3						
4						

Vernier

Angling for Access *(continued)*

◆ Analyze and Conclude

Write your answers on the back of this sheet or on a separate sheet of paper.

1. How did the ideal mechanical advantage and the actual mechanical advantage compare each time you repeated the experiment? Explain your answer.

2. Why do you write ideal and actual mechanical advantage without units?

3. What happens to the mechanical advantage as the inclined plane gets steeper? On the basis of this fact alone, which of the four inclined planes models the best steepness for a wheelchair-access ramp?

4. What other factors, besides mechanical advantage, should you consider when deciding on the steepness of the ramp?

5. **Apply** Suppose the door of the local public library is 2 m above the ground and the distance from the door to the parking lot is 15 m. How would these conditions affect your decision about how steep to make the ramp?

◆ Getting Involved

Find actual ramps that provide access for people with disabilities. Measure the heights and lengths of these ramps and calculate their ideal mechanical advantages. Find out what the requirements are for access ramps in your area. Should your ramp be made of a particular material? Should it level off before it reaches the door? How wide should it be? How does it provide water drainage?

Vernier

Vernier version

Heart Beat, Health Beat

◆ **Problem** How does physical activity affect your pulse rate?

◆ **Materials**

Vernier Exercise Heart Rate Monitor
Logger *Pro* computer software

◆ **Procedure** 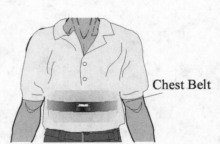 *Review the safety guidelines in Appendix A.*

1. Predict how your heart rate will change as you go from resting to being active, then back to resting again. Then copy the data table into your notebook.

2. Start the Logger *Pro* computer software. Prepare for data collection by opening the experiment file "Heart Beat Health Beat."

3. Plug the receiver module of the heart rate monitor into the first channel of the LabPro interface.

4. Depending upon your size, select a small or large size elastic strap. Secure one of the plastic ends of the elastic strap to the transmitter belt. It is important that the strap provide a snug fit of the transmitter belt.

5. Wet each of the electrodes (the two grooved rectangular areas on the underside of the transmitter belt) with 3 drops of saline solution.

6. Secure the transmitter belt against the skin directly over the base of the rib cage. The POLAR logo on the front of the belt should be centered. Adjust the elastic strap to ensure a tight fit.

Chest Belt

7. Take the receiver module of the heart rate monitor in your right hand and stand as far from the computer monitor as possible. Stand quietly. Remember that the receiver must be within 80 cm of the transmitter in the heart rate monitor belt.

8. Once the subject has been standing quietly for about a minute, a partner should click ▶Start to begin monitoring heart rate. Stand quietly for 60 seconds. **CAUTION:** *Do not complete the rest of these procedures if there is any medical reason why you should avoid physical activities.*

Heart Beat, Health Beat *(continued)*

9. When 60 seconds have gone by, begin to walk in place. It is necessary to walk in place for 60 seconds.

10. After 60 seconds of walking, begin running in place. Continue to run in place for 60 seconds.

11. After 60 seconds of running in place, stop running. Sit down right away and remain so until data collection stops. Data collection will end after you have rested for a total of 4 minutes.

12. Determine the resting heart rate.
  a. Move the mouse pointer to the 0-second line.
  b. Press the mouse button and hold it down as you drag across the graph to the 60-second line to select this part of the graph.
  c. Click on the Statistics button, 🔲. Record the mean (average) resting heart rate (in bpm) in your data table.

13. Determine the heart rate after walking.
  a. Select Examine from the Analyze menu.
  b. Move the cursor to the highest point between 60 and 120 seconds on the graph.
  c. Record the heart rate (HRT) displayed for this point.

14. Determine the heart rate after running.
  a. Select Examine from the Analyze menu.
  b. Move the cursor to the highest point between 120 and 180 seconds on the graph.
  c. Record the heart rate (HRT) displayed for this point.

15. Determine the heart rate after resting for 1 minute.
  a. Move the cursor to the point at 240 seconds on the graph.
  b. Record the heart rate (HRT) displayed for this point.

16. Determine the heart rate after resting for 3 minutes.
  a. Move the cursor to the last point on the graph.
  b. Record the heart rate (HRT) displayed for this point.

17. Print copies of the graph as directed by your teacher.

Vernier

Heart Beat, Health Beat *(continued)*

◆ Data Table

Activity	Pulse Rate
Resting	
Walking	
Running	
Resting after Exercise	
(1 min) Resting after Exercise	
(3+ min) Resting after Exercise	

◆ Analyze and Conclude

Write your answers on the back of this sheet or on a separate sheet of paper.

1. Use the data you obtained to create a bar graph of your pulse rate under the different conditions you tested.

2. What conclusion can you draw about the relationship between physical activity and a person's pulse rate?

3. What happens to the pulse rate when the physical activity has stopped?

4. What can you infer about the heart beat when the pulse rate increases?

5. **Think About It** Do you think the pulse measurements you made are completely accurate? Why or why not? How could you improve the accuracy of your measurements?

◆ Design an Experiment

Do the resting pulse rates of adults, teens, and young children differ? Write a plan to answer this question. Obtain your teacher's permission before carrying out your plan.

© Prentice-Hall, Inc.

Vernier

Vernier version

Heating Earth's Surface

In this lab, you will develop and test a hypothesis about how quickly different materials absorb radiation.

◆ Problem

How do the heating and cooling rates of sand and water compare?

◆ Materials

2 Vernier Temperature Probes	2 beakers, 400 mL
Logger *Pro* computer program	metric ruler
ring stand and 2 ring clamps	lamp with 150-W bulb
sand, 300 mL	string
water, 300 mL	

◆ Procedure   *Review the safety guidelines in Appendix A.*

1. Do you think sand or water will heat up faster? Record your hypothesis on a separate sheet of paper. Explain what information you used to form your hypothesis. Then follow these steps to test your hypothesis.

2. Use the data table to record your data.

3. Start the Logger *Pro* computer software. Prepare for data collection by opening the experiment file "Heating Earth's Surface." Be sure to open the file that matches the probe you are using.

4. Fill one beaker with 300 mL of dry sand.

5. Fill the second beaker with 300 mL of water at room temperature.

6. Arrange the beakers beneath the ring stand.

7. Place one temperature probe in each beaker.

8. Suspend the temperature probes from the ring stand with string. This will hold the probes in place so they do not fall.

9. Adjust the height of the clamp so that the tip of each probe is covered by about 0.5 cm of sand or water in a beaker.

10. Position the lamp so that it is about 20 cm above the sand and water. There should be no more than 8 cm between the beakers. **CAUTION:** *Be careful not to splash water onto the hot light bulb.*

11. Click on ▶Start to begin data collection. Switch on the light bulb. Data collection will end automatically after 15 minutes.

Vernier

Heating Earth's Surface (continued)

12. Record your beginning and final temperatures. Click on the Statistics button, [⊔̃/STAT], then click on [OK] to display a Statistics box for each probe.

13. Move your data to a stored run. To do this, select Store Latest Run from the Data menu.

14. Which material do you think will cool off more quickly? Record your hypothesis on a separate sheet of paper. Again, give reasons why you think your hypothesis is correct.

15. Turn the light off. Repeat Steps 10–11 to test your hypothesis for cooling.

16. Print copies of the graph as directed by your teacher.

◆ Data Table

Temperature with Light On (°C)			Temperature with Light Off (°C)		
Time (min)	Sand	Water	Time (min)	Sand	Water
Start			16		
1			17		
2			18		
3			19		
4			20		
5			21		
6			22		
7			23		
8			24		
9			25		
10			26		
11			27		
12			28		
13			29		
14			30		
15					

Heating Earth's Surface *(continued)*

◆ Analyze and Conclude

Write your answers on a separate sheet of paper.

1. Calculate the total change in temperature for each material.

2. Based on your data, which material had the greater increase in temperature?

3. What can you conclude about which material absorbed heat faster? How do your results compare with your hypothesis?

4. Review your data again. In 15 minutes, which material cooled faster?

5. How do these results compare to your second hypothesis?

6. **Think About It** If your results did not support either of your hypotheses, why do you think the results differed from what you expected?

7. **Apply** Based on your results, which do you think will heat up more quickly on a sunny day: the water in a lake or the sand surrounding it? Which will cool off more quickly after dark?

◆ More to Explore

Do you think all solid materials heat up as fast as sand? For example, consider gravel, crushed stone, or different types of soil. Write a hypothesis about their heating rates. With the approval and supervision of your teacher, develop a procedure to test your hypothesis. Was your hypothesis correct?

Vernier

Just Add Water

If you add hot water to cold water, what will happen? In this lab, you'll make a
device that measures changes in thermal energy. It is called a calorimeter. You will
use the skill of interpreting data to calculate the thermal energy transferred.

◆ **Problem** When hot and cold water are mixed, how much thermal energy
is transferred from the hot water to the cold water?

◆ **Materials**

Vernier Temperature Probe   balance
Logger *Pro* computer software   pencil
4 plastic foam cups   beaker of water kept in an ice bath
hot tap water   scissors

Making a Calorimeter

A. Label a plastic foam cup with the letter C ("C" stands for cold water).
B. Cut 2 to 3 cm from the top of a second plastic foam cup. Invert the second cup
over the first. Label the cover with a C also. The cup and cover are your cold water
calorimeter.
C. Using a pencil, poke a hole in the cover large enough for a temperature probe
to fit snugly.
D. Repeat Steps A, B, and C with two other plastic foam cups. This time, label both
cup and cover with an H. This is your hot water calorimeter.

◆ **Procedure** *Review the safety guidelines in Appendix A.*

1. Predict how the amount of thermal energy lost by hot water will be related to
   the amount of thermal energy gained by cold water.

2. Record all data in the data table.

3. Follow the instructions in the box to make two calorimeters. Find the mass of
   each empty calorimeter (including the cover) on a balance and record each
   mass in your data table.

4. Plug the temperature probe into Channel 1 of the LabPro interface.

5. Start the Logger *Pro* computer software. Prepare for data collection by
   opening the experiment file "Just Add Water." Be sure to open the file that
   matches the probe you are using.

JUST ADD WATER *(continued)*

6. From a beaker of water that has been sitting in an ice bath, add water (no ice cubes) to the cold-water calorimeter. Fill it about one third full. Put the cover on, find the total mass, and record the mass in your data table.

7. Add hot tap water to the hot-water calorimeter. Fill it about one third full. **CAUTION:** *Hot tap water can cause burns.* Put the cover on, find the total mass, and record the mass in your data table.

8. Calculate the mass of the water in each calorimeter. Record the results in your data table.

9. Put the temperature probe through the hole in the cover of the cold-water calorimeter. Wait 30 seconds and then click on ▶Start to begin data collection. Click on the Statistics button, [STAT], to display the statistics for the temperature data. Record the average (mean) temperature of the calorimeter in your data table.

10. Repeat Step 9 for the hot-water calorimeter.

11. Remove the temperature probe and both covers. Pour the water from the cold-water calorimeter into the hot-water calorimeter. Put the cover back on the hot-water calorimeter, and repeat Step 9 to find the temperature. Record the temperature as the final temperature for both calorimeters.

◆ Data Table

	Mass of Empty Cup (g)	Mass of Cup and Water (g)	Mass of Water (g)	Starting Temp. (°C)	Final Temp. (°C)	Change in Temp. (°C)
Cold Water Calorimeter						
Hot Water Calorimeter						

Vernier

JUST ADD WATER *(continued)*

◆ Analyze and Conclude

Write your answers on the back of this sheet or on a separate sheet of paper.

1. What is the temperature change of the cold water? Record your answer in the data table.

2. What is the temperature change of the hot water? Record your answer in the data table.

3. Calculate the amount of thermal energy that enters the cold water by using the formula for the transfer of thermal energy. The specific heat of water is 4.18 J/(g•K), so you use the following formula.

   Thermal energy transferred = 4.18 J/(g•K) × Mass of cold water × Temperature change of cold water. Remember that 1°C is equal to 1 K.

4. Now use the formula to calculate the thermal energy leaving the hot water.

5. What unit should you use for your results for Questions 3 and 4?

6. Was your prediction from Step 1 confirmed? How do you know?

7. **Think About It** What sources of error might have affected your results? How could the lab be redesigned in order to reduce the errors?

◆ Design an Experiment

How would your results be affected if you started with much more hot water than cold? If you used more cold water than hot? Make a prediction. Then design a procedure to test your prediction. Get your teacher's approval, and try your new procedure.

Vernier

Keeping Comfortable

Two ways to use less energy are to keep heat out of your home when the weather is hot, and to keep heat in when the weather is cold. In this lab, you will design an experiment to compare how well different materials do this.

◆ Problem   How well do different materials stop heat transfer?

◆ Suggested Materials

Vernier Temperature Probe
Logger *Pro* computer software
hot water
ice water
beakers
containers and lids made of paper, plastic foam, plastic, glass, and metal

◆ Design a Plan   *Review the safety guidelines in Appendix A.*

◆ Part 1 Measuring Temperature Changes

1. Plug the temperature probe into Channel 1 of the LabPro interface.

2. Start the Logger *Pro* computer software. Prepare for data collection by opening the experiment file "Keeping Comfortable." Be sure to open the file that matches the probe you are using.

3. Use a pencil to poke a hole in the lid of a paper cup. Fill the cup about halfway with cold water.

4. Put the lid on the cup. Insert a temperature probe into the water through the hole. When the temperature stops dropping, place the cup in a beaker. Add hot water to the beaker until the water level is about 1 cm below the lid.

5. Click on `▶Start` to begin data collection. Continue collecting data until the temperature has increased by 5°C. Click on `■Stop` to end data collection. Use the time it takes for the temperature to increase 1°C as a measure of the effectiveness of the paper cup.

Vernier

KEEPING COMFORTABLE (*continued*)

◆ Part 2 Comparing Materials

6. Use the ideas from Part 1 to design a controlled experiment to rank the effectiveness of different materials in preventing heat transfer.

7. Use the following questions to help you plan your experiment. Write your plan on the next page.
   - ◆ What hypothesis will you test?
   - ◆ Which materials do you predict will be the best and worst at preventing heat transfer?
   - ◆ What will your manipulated variable be? What will your responding variable be?
   - ◆ What variables do you need to control? How will you control them?
   - ◆ What step-by-step procedures will you use?
   - ◆ What kind of data table will you use?

8. After your teacher has reviewed your plans, make any necessary changes in your design. Then perform your experiment.

◆ Analyze and Conclude

Write your answers on a separate sheet of paper.

1. In Part 1, what was the starting temperature of the hot water? What was the starting temperature of the cold water? In which direction did the heat flow? How do you know?

2. If the materials in Part 1 are used to represent your home in very hot weather, which material would represent the rooms in your home? Which would represent the outdoor weather? Which would represent the walls of the building?

3. Which material was most effective at blocking the transfer of heat? Which was the least effective? Explain.

4. **Think About It** Would experiments similar to this one provide you with enough information to choose materials to build a home? Explain.

◆ More to Explore

Create a plan to compare how well the materials would work if the hot water were inside the cup and the cold water were outside. With your teacher's permission, carry out your plan.

Vernier

KEEPING COMFORTABLE *(continued)*

EXPERIMENT PLAN

Write your experiment plan below. If you need more room, use a separate sheet of paper.

◆ **Hypothesis**

_____

_____

◆ **Materials**

_____

_____

_____

_____

◆ **Procedure**

_____

_____

_____

_____

_____

_____

_____

◆ **Data Table**

Vernier

Melting Ice

In this experiment, you will measure temperature as you explore the melting of ice.

◆ **Problem** How does the temperature of the surroundings affect the rate at which ice melts?

◆ **Materials**

Vernier Temperature Probe
Logger *Pro* computer software
plastic cup, about 200 mL
ice cubes, about 2 cm on each side
warm water, about 40°C to 45°C
water at room temperature, about 20°C

◆ **Procedure**   *Review the safety guidelines in Appendix A.*

1. Read Steps 1–12. Based on your own experience, predict which ice cube will melt faster.

2. In your notebook, make a data table like the one below.

3. Plug the temperature probe into Channel 1 of the LabPro interface.

4. Start the Logger *Pro* computer software. Prepare for data collection by opening the experiment file "Melting Ice." Be sure to open the file that matches the probe you are using.

5. Fill a cup halfway with warm water (about 40°C to 45°C).

6. Record the exact temperature of the water in the cup.

7. Obtain an ice cube that is roughly the same size as the other available ice cubes. Place the ice cube in the cup of water and click on ⟨▶Collect⟩ to begin data collection.

8. Using the temperature probe, gently stir the water in the cup until the ice cube in the cup has completely melted. Click on ⟨■Stop⟩ to end data collection.

9. Record the time it took for the ice cube to melt and the final water temperature in your data table.

MELTING ICE (continued)

10. Move your data to a stored run. To do this, select Store Latest Run from the Data menu.

11. Empty the water from the cup. Fill the cup halfway with water at room temperature.

12. Repeat Steps 6–9 to collect data.

13. Print copies of the graph as directed by your teacher.

◆ Data Table

	Beginning Temperature (°C)	Time to Melt (s)	Final Temperature (°C)
Cup 1			
Cup 2			

◆ Analyze and Conclude

Write your answers on the back of this sheet or on a separate sheet of paper.

1. Was your prediction in Step 1 supported by the results of the experiment? Explain why or why not.

2. In which cup did the water temperature change the most? Explain this result.

3. When the ice melted, its molecules gained enough energy to overcome the forces holding them together as solid ice. What is the source of that energy?

4. **Think About It** How well could you time the exact moment that each ice cube completely melted? How might errors in measurements affect your conclusions?

◆ Design an Experiment

When a lake freezes in winter, only the top layer turns to ice. Design an experiment to model the melting of a frozen lake during spring. With your teacher's approval, carry out your experiment. Be prepared to share your results with the class.

© Prentice-Hall, Inc.

Vernier

Shedding Light on Chemical Bonds

Electricity is the flow of electric current. In this lab, you will interpret data about which compounds conduct electricity in order to determine the nature of their bonds.

◆ **Problem**   How can you use a conductivity tester to determine whether a compound contains ionic or covalent bonds?

◆ **Materials**

Vernier Conductivity Probe	graduated cylinder, 100 mL
Logger *Pro* computer software	small plastic spoon
small beaker	table salt
distilled water	additional substances provided by your teacher

◆ **Procedure**   *Review the safety guidelines in Appendix A.*

1. Make a data table in your notebook similar to the one shown on the next page.

2. Set up the conductivity probe with the ring stand and utility clamp as shown.

3. Plug the conductivity probe into Channel 1 of the LabPro interface. Set the switch on the side of the conductivity probe box to the 0–20,000 range.

4. Start the Logger *Pro* computer software. Prepare for data collection by opening the experiment file "Chemical Bonds." Be sure to open the file that matches the probe you are using.

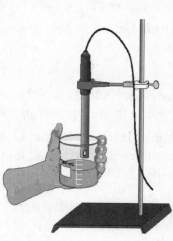

5. Testing the conductivity of distilled water.
   a. Pour 200 mL of distilled water in a beaker and place the conductivity probe into it.
   b. The hole near the probe end must be completely submerged in the solution.
   c. Click on [▶Collect] to begin a 10-second sampling run. *Important:* Leave the probe tip submerged for the 10 seconds that data is being collected.
   d. Click on the Statistics button, [STAT], to display the statistics box on the graph.
   e. A statistics box will appear on the graph. Record the mean conductivity reading in your data table.
   f. To avoid contaminating the solutions, rinse the probe with clean, distilled water after each test. Blot the outside of the probe dry with a tissue or paper towel. Do not worry about drying the inside of the hole near the tip of the probe.

SHEDDING LIGHT ON CHEMICAL BONDS *(continued)*

6. Add a very small scoop of salt (1/8 teaspoon) to the beaker of distilled water. Stir the salt into the water until completely dissolved.

7. Repeat Step 5 using the salt water you just mixed.

8. Repeat Step 5 for each substance provided by your teacher.

- ◆ If the substance is a solid, mix a small spoonful (1/8 teaspoon) of it with about 200 mL of distilled water. Test the resulting mixture.

- ◆ If the substance is a liquid, simply pour about 100 mL into an empty beaker. Test it as you did the mixtures of solids in water.

◆ Data Table

Sample	Conductivity	Ionic or Covalent Bonds
Water		
Sodium chloride in water		

Vernier

SHEDDING LIGHT ON CHEMICAL BONDS *(continued)*

◆ Analyze and Conclude

Write your answers on the back of this sheet or on a separate sheet of paper.

1. Why did you test plain water first?

2. Based on your observations, indicate whether each substance tested contained ionic or covalent bonds.

3. Explain why one substance is a better conductor of electricity than another.

4. Did all the substances that conducted electricity show the same amount of conductivity? If not, what might have caused the differences?

5. **Think About It** How might varying the amount of each substance added to the water have affected your results? How could you better control the amount of each substance?

◆ Design an Experiment

Design another experiment to compare a different property of compounds containing ionic and covalent bonds. You might want to examine properties such as melting point, whether the substances dissolve in water, or whether the substances dissolve in some other liquid. Present your experimental plan to your teacher before proceeding.

Vernier

Sticky Sneakers

The appropriate sneaker for an activity should have a specific type of tread to grip the floor or the ground. In this lab you will test different sneakers by measuring the amount of friction between the sneakers and a table.

◆ **Problem** How does the amount of friction between a sneaker and a surface compare for different types of sneakers?

◆ **Skills Focus** forming operational definitions, measuring, controlling variables

◆ **Materials**

three or more different types of sneakers
Vernier Dual-Range Force Sensor   large paper clip
Logger *Pro* computer software   tape
mass set(s)   balance

◆ **Procedure** 🦶 *Review the safety guidelines in Appendix A.*

1. Sneakers are designed to deal with various friction forces, including these:
   ◆ starting friction, which is involved when you start from a stopped position
   ◆ forward-stopping friction, which is involved when you come to a forward stop
   ◆ sideways-stopping friction, which is involved when you come to a sideways stop

2. Use the data table to record your data.

3. Find the mass of each sneaker. Then put masses in each sneaker so that the total mass of the sneaker plus the masses is 1000 g. Spread the masses out evenly inside the sneaker.

4. Start the Logger *Pro* computer software. Prepare for data collection by opening the experiment file "Sticky Sneakers." Be sure to open the file that matches the probe you are using.

© Prentice-Hall, Inc.

Vernier

STICKY SNEAKERS *(continued)*

5. You will need to tape the paper clip to each sneaker and then attach a force sensor to the paper clip. To measure
   - ◆ starting friction, attach the paper clip to the back of the sneaker.
   - ◆ forward-stopping friction, attach the paper clip to the front of the sneaker.
   - ◆ sideways-stopping friction, attach the paper clip to the side of the sneaker.

6. To measure starting friction, click on [▶Collect] to begin data collection and slowly pull the sneaker backward with the force sensor until it starts to move.

7. The force necessary to make the sneaker start moving is equal to the friction force. When data collection is finished, click on the examine button, [⬚]. Move the mouse cursor to the highest peak on your graph. This is the starting-friction force. Record the starting-friction force in your data table.

8. To measure either type of stopping friction, slowly pull the sneaker across the table at a constant speed. Once the sneaker is moving at a steady rate, click on [▶Collect] to begin data collection. Click on the Statistics button, [⬚], and record the mean force (stopping-friction force) in your data table.

9. Repeat Steps 5–8 for the remaining sneakers.

◆ Data Table

Sneaker (N)	Starting Friction	Sideways-Stopping Friction (N)	Forward-Stopping Friction (N)
A			
B			
C			
D			
E			
F			

STICKY SNEAKERS *(continued)*

◆ Analyze and Conclude

Answer the following questions on the back of this sheet or on a separate sheet of paper.

1. What are the manipulated and responding variables in this experiment? Explain.

2. Why is the reading of the force sensor equal to the friction force in each case?

3. Do you think that using a sneaker with a small amount of mass in it is a fair test of the friction of the sneakers? (Consider the fact that sneakers are used with people's feet inside them.) Explain your answer.

4. Draw a diagram that shows the forces acting on the sneaker for each type of motion.

5. Why did you pull the sneaker at a slow speed to test for stopping friction? For starting friction, why did you pull a sneaker that wasn't moving?

6. Which sneaker had the most starting friction? Which had the most forward-stopping friction? Which had the most sideways-stopping friction?

7. Can you identify a relationship between the type of sneaker and the type of friction you observed? What do you observe about the sneakers that would cause one to have better traction than another?

8. **Apply** Wear a pair of your own sneakers. Start running and notice how you press against the floor with your sneaker. How do you think this affects the friction between the sneaker and the floor? How can you test for this variable?

◆ Getting Involved

Go to a store that sells sneakers. If possible take a spring scale and, with the clerk's permission, do a quick friction test on sneakers designed for different activities. Also, note the materials they are made of, the support they provide for your feet, and other features. Then decide whether it is necessary to buy specific sneakers for different activities.

Vernier

Sunny Rays and Angles

In this lab, you will investigate how the angle of the sun's rays affects the amount of energy absorbed by different parts of Earth's surface.

◆ **Problem** How does the angle of a light source affect the rate of temperature change of a surface?

◆ **Materials**

3 Vernier Temperature Probes   pencil
Logger *Pro* computer software   metric ruler
books   100-W incandescent lamp
scissors   clear tape
black construction paper   protractor

◆ **Procedure**   *Review the safety guidelines in Appendix A.*

1. Cut a strip of black construction paper 5 cm by 10 cm. Fold the paper in half and tape two sides to form a pocket.

2. Repeat Step 1 to make two more pockets.

3. Place the tip of a temperature probe inside each pocket.

4. Place the pockets with temperature probes close together as shown in the figure below. Place one probe in a vertical position (90° angle), one at a 45° angle, and the third one in a horizontal position (0° angle). Use a protractor to measure the angles. Support the probes with books.

5. Position the lamp so that it is 30 cm from each of the probe tips. Make sure the lamp will not move during the activity.

6. Use the data table on the next page to record your data.

7. Plug Temperature Probe 1 into Channel 1 of the LabPro interface. Plug Temperature Probe 2 into Channel 2. Plug Temperature Probe 3 into Channel 3.

8. Start the Logger *Pro* computer software. Prepare for data collection by opening the experiment file "Sunny Rays." Be sure to open the file that matches the probes you are using.

SUNNY RAYS AND ANGLES *(continued)*

9. In the data table, record the current temperature of all three temperature probes. (All three temperatures should be similar.)

10. Switch on the lamp. Click on ⬛ to begin data collection. In the data table, record the temperature of each probe every minute for 15 minutes.
CAUTION: *Be careful not to touch the hot lampshade.*

11. Data collection will end automatically after 15 minutes. When this happens, switch off the lamp.

◆ Data Table

Time (min.)	Temperature (°C)		
	0° Angle	45° Angle	90° Angle
Start			
1			
2			
3			
4			
5			
6			
7			
8			
9			
10			
11			
12			
13			
14			
15			

Vernier

SUNNY RAYS AND ANGLES *(continued)*

◆ Analyze and Conclude

Write your answers on the back of this sheet or on a separate sheet of paper.

1. In this experiment, what was the manipulated variable? What was the responding variable? How do you know which is which?

2. Graph your data on a sheet of graph paper. Label the horizontal axis time (min.) and vertical axis temperature (°C). Use solid, dashed, and dotted lines to show the results from each thermometer.

3. Based on your data, at which angle did the temperature increase the most?

4. At which angle did the temperature increase the least?

5. What part of Earth's surface does each temperature probe represent?

6. Why is air at the North Pole still very cold in the summer even though the Northern Hemisphere is tilted toward the sun?

7. **Think About It** In this experiment, what variables were held constant?

◆ Design an Experiment

Design an experiment to find out how the results of this investigation would change if the lamp were placed farther away from the temperature probes. Then design another experiment to find out what would happen if the lamp were placed closer to the temperature probes.

Vernier

Appendix A
Laboratory Safety

Safety Symbols

These symbols alert you to possible dangers in the laboratory and remind you to work carefully.

Safety Goggles Always wear safety goggles to protect your eyes in any activity involving chemicals, flames or heating, or the possibility of broken glassware.

Lab Apron Wear a laboratory apron to protect your skin and clothing from damage.

Breakage You are working with materials that may be breakable, such as glass containers, glass tubing, thermometers, or funnels. Handle breakable materials with care. Do not touch broken glassware.

Heat-Resistant Gloves Use an oven mitt or other hand protection when handling hot materials. Hot plates, hot glassware, or hot water can cause burns. Do not touch hot objects with your bare hands.

Heating Use a clamp or tongs to pick up hot glassware. Do not touch hot objects with your bare hands.

Sharp Object Pointed-tip scissors, scalpels, knives, needles, pins, or tacks are sharp. They can cut or puncture your skin. Always direct a sharp edge or point away from yourself and others. Use sharp instruments only as instructed.

Electric Shock Avoid the possibility of electric shock. Never use electrical equipment around water, or when the equipment is wet or your hands are wet. Be sure cords are untangled and cannot trip anyone. Disconnect the equipment when it is not in use.

Corrosive Chemical You are working with an acid or another corrosive chemical. Avoid getting it on your skin or clothing, or in your eyes. Do not inhale the vapors. Wash your hands when you are finished with the activity.

Poison Do not let any poisonous chemical come in contact with your skin, and do not inhale its vapors. Wash your hands when you are finished with the activity.

Physical Safety When an experiment involves physical activity, take precautions to avoid injuring yourself or others. Follow instructions from your teacher. Alert your teacher if there is any reason you should not participate in the activity.

Flames You may be working with flames from a lab burner, candle, or matches. Tie back loose hair and clothing. Follow instructions from your teacher about lighting and extinguishing flames.

No Flames Flammable materials may be present. Make sure there are no flames, sparks, or other exposed heat sources present.

Fumes When poisonous or unpleasant vapors may be involved, work in a ventilated area. Avoid inhaling vapors directly. Only test an odor when directed to do so by your teacher, and use a wafting motion to direct the vapor toward your nose.

Disposal Chemicals and other laboratory materials used in the activity must be disposed of safely. Follow the instructions from your teacher.

Hand Washing Wash your hands thoroughly when finished with the activity. Use antibacterial soap and warm water. Lather both sides of your hands and between your fingers. Rinse well.

General Safety Awareness You may see this symbol when none of the symbols described earlier appears. In this case, follow the specific instructions provided. You may also see this symbol when you are asked to develop your own procedure in a lab. Have your teacher approve your plan before you go further.

Science Safety Rules

To prepare yourself to work safely in the laboratory, read over the following safety rules. Then read them a second time. Make sure you understand and follow each rule. Ask your teacher to explain any rules you do not understand.

Dress Code

1. To protect yourself from injuring your eyes, wear safety goggles whenever you work with chemicals, burners, glassware, or any substance that might get into your eyes. If you wear contact lenses, notify your teacher.
2. Wear a lab apron or coat whenever you work with corrosive chemicals or substances that can stain.
3. Tie back long hair to keep it away from any chemicals, flames, or equipment.
4. Remove or tie back any article of clothing or jewelry that can hang down and touch chemicals, flames, or equipment. Roll up or secure long sleeves.
5. Never wear open shoes or sandals.

General Precautions

6. Read all directions for an experiment several times before beginning the activity. Carefully follow all written and oral instructions. If you are in doubt about any part of the experiment, ask your teacher for assistance.
7. Never perform activities that are not assigned or authorized by your teacher. Obtain permission before "experimenting" on your own. Never handle any equipment unless you have specific permission.
8. Never perform lab activities without direct supervision.
9. Never eat or drink in the laboratory.
10. Keep work areas clean and tidy at all times. Bring only notebooks and lab manuals or written lab procedures to the work area. All other items, such as purses and backpacks, should be left in a designated area.
11. Do not engage in horseplay.

First Aid

12. Always report all accidents or injuries to your teacher, no matter how minor. Notify your teacher immediately about any fires.
13. Learn what to do in case of specific accidents, such as getting acid in your eyes or on your skin. (Rinse acids from your body with lots of water.)
14. Be aware of the location of the first-aid kit, but do not use it unless instructed by your teacher. In case of injury, your teacher should administer first aid. Your teacher may also send you to the school nurse or call a physician.
15. Know the location of emergency equipment, such as the fire extinguisher and fire blanket, and know how to use it.
16. Know the location of the nearest telephone and whom to contact in an emergency.

Heating and Fire Safety

17. Never use a heat source, such as a candle, burner, or hot plate, without wearing safety goggles.
18. Never heat anything unless instructed to do so. A chemical that is harmless when cool may be dangerous when heated.
19. Keep all combustible materials away from flames. Never use a flame or spark near a combustible chemical.
20. Never reach across a flame.
21. Before using a laboratory burner, make sure you know proper procedures for lighting and adjusting the burner, as demonstrated by your teacher. Do not touch the burner. It may be hot. And never leave a lighted burner unattended!
22. Chemicals can splash or boil out of a heated test tube. When heating a substance in a test tube, make sure that the mouth of the tube is not pointed at you or anyone else.
23. Never heat a liquid in a closed container. The expanding gases produced may blow the container apart.
24. Before picking up a container that has been heated, hold the back of your hand near it. If you can feel heat on the back of your hand, the container is too hot to handle. Use an oven mitt to pick up a container that has been heated.

Using Chemicals Safely

25. Never mix chemicals "for the fun of it." You might produce a dangerous, possibly explosive substance.
26. Never put your face near the mouth of a container that holds chemicals. Many chemicals are poisonous. Never touch, taste, or smell a chemical unless you are instructed by your teacher to do so.
27. Use only those chemicals needed in the activity. Read and double-check labels on supply bottles before removing any chemicals. Take only as much as you need. Keep all containers closed when chemicals are not being used.
28. Dispose of all chemicals as instructed by your teacher. To avoid contamination, never return chemicals to their original containers. Never simply pour chemicals or other substances into the sink or trash containers.
29. Be extra careful when working with acids or bases. Pour all chemicals over the sink or a container, not over your work surface.
30. If you are instructed to test for odors, use a wafting motion to direct the odors to your nose. Do not inhale the fumes directly from the container.
31. When mixing an acid and water, always pour the water into the container first and then add the acid to the water. Never pour water into an acid.
32. Take extreme care not to spill any material in the laboratory. Wash chemical spills and splashes immediately with plenty of water. Immediately begin rinsing with water any acids that get on your skin or clothing, and notify your teacher of any acid spill at the same time.

Using Glassware Safely

33. Never force glass tubing or thermometers into a rubber stopper or rubber tubing. Have your teacher insert the glass tubing or thermometer if required for an activity.
34. If you are using a laboratory burner, use a wire screen to protect glassware from any flame. Never heat glassware that is not thoroughly dry on the outside.
35. Keep in mind that hot glassware looks cool. Never pick up glassware without first checking to see if it is hot. Use an oven mitt. See Rule 24.
36. Never use broken or chipped glassware. If glassware breaks, notify your teacher and dispose of the glassware in the proper broken-glassware container. Never handle broken glass with your bare hands.
37. Never eat or drink from lab glassware.
38. Thoroughly clean glassware before putting it away.

Using Sharp Instruments

39. Handle scalpels or other sharp instruments with extreme care. Never cut material toward you; cut away from you.
40. Immediately notify your teacher if you cut your skin when working in the laboratory.

Animal and Plant Safety

41. Never perform experiments that cause pain, discomfort, or harm to animals. This rule applies at home as well as in the classroom.
42. Animals should be handled only if absolutely necessary. Your teacher will instruct you as to how to handle each animal species brought into the classroom.
43. If you know that you are allergic to certain plants, molds, or animals, tell your teacher before doing an activity in which these are used.
44. During field work, protect your skin by wearing long pants, long sleeves, socks, and closed shoes. Know how to recognize the poisonous plants and fungi in your area, as well as plants with thorns, and avoid contact with them. Never eat any part of a plant or fungus.
45. Wash your hands thoroughly after handling animals or a cage containing animals. Wash your hands when you are finished with any activity involving animal parts, plants, or soil.

End-of-Experiment Rules

46. After an experiment has been completed, turn off all burners or hot plates. If you used a gas burner, check that the gas-line valve to the burner is off. Unplug hot plates.
47. Turn off and unplug any other electrical equipment that you used.
48. Clean up your work area and return all equipment to its proper place.
49. Dispose of waste materials as instructed by your teacher.
50. Wash your hands after every experiment.

Appendix B
Teacher Notes and Answers

Angling for Access

Analyze and Conclude

1. The actual mechanical advantage is always less than the ideal mechanical advantage because of the friction between the block or cart and the incline.
2. Ideal mechanical advantage is obtained by dividing the length of incline by the height of incline. The units of distance (centimeters) cancel out. Actual mechanical advantage is obtained by dividing the output force by the input force. The units of force (newtons) cancel out.
3. The mechanical advantage decreases as the ramp gets steeper. On this basis alone, one would choose the least steep ramp.
4. Answers may vary. Sample: If the ramp is too gradual it may be too long to be feasible. If the ramp is too steep, it will be dangerous.
5. **Apply** Unless the ramp doubled back on itself, the shallowness of the ramp would be limited by those conditions. The best possible ideal mechanical advantage would be $15 \div 2 = 7.5$.

Extending the Inquiry

Getting Involved Students may have difficulty measuring the length and height of their ramps. Explain that only the ratio of length to height determines the ideal mechanical advantage, and that this ratio is the same for all or part of the ramp. Students can work with only part of the ramp if that is more feasible. When interviewing people who use access ramps, students should prepare a series of questions in advance. Students should explain what they are doing and why, so that people will be more inclined to respond to their requests for an interview.

For more information on this activity, watch the *Science Explorer* Lab Activity Videotape for this lab.

Heart Beat, Health Beat

Safety

Students with medical reasons to avoid exercise should do only Steps 1–9.

Expected Outcome

Pulse should increase more when running than walking, then return to a resting rate (70–80 beats per minute).

Analyze and Conclude

1. Graphs should be clearly labeled.
2. Pulse rate increases during exercise.
3. The pulse returns to the resting rate.
4. The heart is beating faster.
5. **Think About It** Answers will vary. Averaging many measurements improves accuracy.

Extending the Inquiry

Design an Experiment Students' plans should include measuring the resting pulse rate of people of different ages.

For more information on this activity, watch the *Science Explorer* Lab Activity Videotape for this lab.

Heating Earth's Surface

Safety

Caution students to be careful not to touch the light bulb or splash water on it. Review the safety guidelines in Appendix A.

Expected Outcome

Students should find that the sand heats and cools more quickly than the water. Both graphs should rise steadily during the first 15 minutes and then decline steadily during the second 15 minutes. The line for sand temperature should rise and fall more steeply than the line for water temperature, indicating a greater rate of change in temperature for sand than water.

Analyze and Conclude

1. Exact answers will vary depending on the specific temperatures recorded. However, the sand should show a greater total change in temperature than the water.
2. The data should show that the sand had a greater increase in temperature.
3. Students should conclude that the sand absorbed heat faster than the water. These results may or may not agree with their hypotheses.
4. The data should show that the sand cooled faster.
5. These results may or may not agree with their second hypotheses.
6. **Think About It** Answers may vary. One possible answer is that they expected both the sand and water to heat and cool at the same rate because there were equal amounts of the two substances.
7. **Apply** Based on their results, students should say that the sand surrounding a lake will heat up more quickly on a sunny day and cool off more quickly after dark than the water in the lake.

Extending the Inquiry

More to Explore Students may think that solids with a different texture, made of different materials, or having different colors might heat up at different rates than sand. For example, students may think that rock would heat up faster than sand because it is more solid. Students may hypothesize that soil will heat up faster than sand because it is darker in color. They can test

their hypotheses by repeating the skills lab and substituting soil or other materials for water.

For more information on this activity, watch the *Science Explorer* Lab Activity Videotape for this lab.

Just Add Water

Expected Outcome

The final temperature should be greater than the initial temperature of the cold water and less than the initial temperature of the hot water. The amount of thermal energy transferred to the cold water should be approximately equal to the thermal energy lost by the hot water, taking into account experimental error and heat lost to the surroundings during transfer.

Analyze and Conclude

1–4. Answers will vary.
5. Joules (J)
6. Answers will depend on the initial predictions. Students should provide logical reasons for why their predictions were or were not confirmed. A typical prediction could state that the thermal energy lost by the hot water will be nearly equal to the thermal energy gained by the cold water. Given experimental error, this prediction will probably be supported. Results usually reflect some difference due to heat lost to the surroundings during transfer.
7. **Think About It** Sources of error include loss of thermal energy in the form of heat through the sides or top of the cup, and misreading the balances. Students may suggest using a thicker cup or a better insulating material, nesting two or more cups inside each other, or repeating the procedure several times and averaging the results.

Extending the Inquiry

Design an Experiment With more hot water, the mixture will end up hotter and with more cold water, the mixture will end up colder.

For more information on this activity, watch the *Science Explorer* Lab Activity Videotape for this lab.

Keeping Comfortable

Safety
Students should use caution in handling the hot water and glass containers. Review the safety guidelines in Appendix A.

Expected Outcome
Plastic foam is most effective for stopping heat transfer; metal, least effective.

Analyze and Conclude
1. Temperatures will vary. Heat flowed from the hot water to the cold water, as shown by the temperature changes.
2. Rooms: cold water; outdoor weather: hot water; walls: paper cup
3. Most effective: plastic foam. Least effective: metal. Plastic foam kept the cold water close to its starting temperature for the longest time, while metal let the starting temperature increase the most.
4. **Think About It** Other issues, such as strength, durability, and cost, must be considered.

Extending the Inquiry
More to Explore Students' plans should be similar to those they developed in Part 2.

For more information on this activity, watch the *Science Explorer* Lab Activity Videotape for this lab.

Melting Ice

Analyze and Conclude
1. Answers will vary.
2. The temperature of the warmer water changed the most, because there was a greater difference between it and the melting point of ice.
3. The thermal energy of the water
4. **Think About It** Answers will vary. Taking the final temperature too late will cause the reading of the final temperature to be closer to room temperature and will increase the time measurement.

Extending the Inquiry
Design an Experiment Students may design experiments similar to this lab. The "lake" could be a partially frozen container of water with a layer of ice on top. One "lake" could be exposed to a lamp (the "lake") while the other is kept in the shade. Check students' plans for safety.

For more information on this activity, watch the *Science Explorer* Lab Activity Videotape for this lab.

Shedding Light on Chemical Bonds

Safety
Liquids that dissolve substances with covalent bonds are often poisonous and flammable. Appropriate ventilation and fire prevention procedures should be followed. Make sure students wear goggles and lab aprons during the lab. Caution students to handle the glass beakers with care. Review the safety guidelines in Appendix A.

Expected Outcome
Most substances containing ionic bonds will conduct electricity fairly well when dissolved in water. Molecular compounds do not conduct electricity well, either as pure liquids or as water solutions.

Analyze and Conclude
1. Plain water was tested as a control and to show that a water solution can conduct electricity only with the presence of an added substance.
2. Sample chart

Sample	Type of Bond
water	covalent
sodium chloride in water	ionic
sugar in water	covalent
vegetable oil	covalent
Epsom salts in water	ionic

3. Compounds containing ionic bonds are better conductors of electricity. When they dissolve, the ions are free to move within a solution. Compounds containing covalent bonds separate into neutral molecules that do not carry electrical charge.

4. Electrical conductivity is indicated by the brightness of the light bulb. Not all substances showed the same brightness, therefore not all showed the same amount of electrical conductivity.
5. **Think About It**   Using different amounts would not change whether a substance conducted electricity, but it might change the amount of conductivity. Using the same mass of each substance in the same volume of water would help control the experiment.

Extending the Inquiry

Design an Experiment   Review students' plans for safety and thoroughness before allowing them to conduct tests. Tests of whether substances dissolve in water and another liquid should use the same volume of liquid and the same mass of each substance.

For more information on this activity, watch the *Science Explorer* Lab Activity Videotape for this lab.

Sticky Sneakers

Expected Outcome
Students should have a table with a column for each kind of friction, showing the force of friction for each kind of sneaker.

Analyze and Conclude
1. Manipulated variable: the sneaker sole
   Responding variable: the amount of friction
2. For stopping friction, the sneaker is moving at a constant speed, therefore, the friction force and the pulling force must be balanced (equal). The pulling force is indicated by the force sensor. For starting friction, the pulling force must overcome the friction force in order to make the sneaker move. At the point where the sneaker starts to move, the two forces are almost equal.
3. It is a fair test of the friction as long as the amount of friction for each sneaker depends on mass in the same way.

4. See students' diagrams. Diagrams should be clearly labeled with force arrows reflecting the size of the force and the direction.
5. You pull the sneaker at a slow speed to test stopping friction because when you stop, the sneaker is sliding slowly along the ground. You pull a sneaker that is not moving for starting friction because when you start running the sneaker is not moving yet.
6. Answers will vary. Running sneakers tend to exhibit more starting friction. Basketball sneakers tend to exert more stopping friction. Tennis shoes tend to exert more sideways-stopping friction.
7. One type of sneaker may provide better traction than another because the soles are made of a different material, they have different treads, or have worn treads or rubber soles hardened with age.
8. **Apply**   When you press against the floor when starting to run, you increase the force with which the sneaker and floor press against each other, increasing the friction force. To test for this variable, students could repeat the lab after adding weights to each sneaker. A suitable weight could be made by filling several resealable plastic bags with sand. These could be stuffed into the sneaker before measuring each type of friction.

Extending the Inquiry

Getting Involved   Remind students they must go to the store with an adult supervisor and ask permission from the store clerk before carrying out the friction test. Remind students to compare sneakers of about the same mass. Students will probably find there are not big differences in friction between different types of sneakers. The same type of sneakers should exhibit about the same amount of each type of friction.

For more information on this activity, watch the *Science Explorer* Lab Activity Videotape for this lab.

Sunny Rays and Angles

Safety

Caution students to be careful when handling the lamp, because the light bulb and the lampshade get hot. Review the safety guidelines in Appendix A.

Expected Outcome

The temperature sensor at the 0° angle will show the highest increase in temperature. The temperature sensor at the 90° angle will show the lowest increase in temperature. The temperature at the 45° angle will show a moderate temperature increase.

Analyze and Conclude

1. The manipulated variable is the angle of the temperature sensor. The responding variable is the rate of temperature change. The responding variable is affected by the changes in the manipulated variable.
2. All three lines of the graph should show an increase in temperature over time. However, the line for the temperature sensor at 0° should show a greater temperature increase than the temperature sensor at 45°, which should show a greater temperature increase than the temperature sensor at 90°.
3. at the 0° angle
4. at the 90° angle
5. The temperature sensor at 0° represents the tropical zone, the temperature sensor at 45° represents the temperate zone, and the temperature sensor at 90° represents the polar zone.
6. Because the angle at which the sun's rays strike the North Pole in summer is still very low
7. Variables that were held constant include the temperature sensors, the heat source, the distance of the heat source from the temperature sensors, and the type of heat-absorbing material of the temperature sensors.

Extending the Inquiry

Design an Experiment Students should use the same procedure, except they should change the distances between the temperature sensors and the lamp.

For more information on this activity, watch the *Science Explorer* Lab Activity Videotape for this lab.